ANCIENT SCIENCE
AND MODERN CIVILIZATION

George Sarton

Ancient Science

and Modern Civilization

UNIVERSITY OF NEBRASKA PRESS · Lincoln

50 X3
52 7 a

CONTENTS

PREFACE   1

EUCLID AND HIS TIME   3

PTOLEMY AND HIS TIME   37

THE END OF GREEK SCIENCE AND CULTURE   75

This book reproduces the full text of the three Montgomery Lectures which it was my privilege to deliver at the University of Nebraska, in Lincoln, on April 19, 21, 23, 1954.

In spite of their name the "lectures" were not read but spoken; the essential of the spoken and written texts is the same, but there are naturally considerable differences in the details. The spoken text is to the written one with its explanatory footnotes like a fresco to a miniature. That must be so, because people cannot listen as accurately as they can read. I have explained my views on this subject many times, last in the preface to my Logan Clendening Lecture on Galen of Pergamon (University of Kansas Press, Lawrence, Kansas, 1954).

As mechanical progress discourages the printing of Greek type, it has become necessary to transcribe the Greek words in our alphabet as exactly as possible. The diphthongs are written as in Greek with the same vowels (e.g., *ai* not *ae*, *ei* not *i*, *oi* not *oe*), except *ou*, which is written *u* to conform with English pronunciation (by the way, the Greek *ou* is not a real diphthong but a single vowel sound). The omicron is always replaced by an *o*, and hence the Greek names are not Latinized but preserve their Greek look and sound. There is really no reason for giving a Latin ending to a Greek name when one is writing not in Latin but in English. Hence, we write Epicuros not Epicurus (the two *u*'s of the Latin word represent different Greek vowels). We indicate the differences between the short vowels epsilon and omicron and the long ones ēta and ōmega, as we have just done in their names. Hence, we shall write Hērōn, Philōn, but some names have become so familiar to English readers that we must write them in the English way. We cannot help writing Plato instead of Platōn and Aristotle instead of Aristotelēs, etc. For more details, see my *History of Science,* p. xvii.

Indications such as (III-2 B.C.) or (II-1) after a name mean two things: (1) the man flourished in the second half of the third century before Christ or in the first half of the second century; (2) he is dealt with in my *Introduction.*

GEORGE SARTON

Harvard University
Cambridge, Massachusetts

2

EUCLID AND HIS TIME

(first half of third century B.C.)

WHAT has ancient science to do with modern civilization? one might ask. Very much. Modern civilization is focused upon science and technology, and modern science is but the continuation of ancient science; it would not exist without the latter. For example, Euclid flourished in Alexandria more than twenty-two centuries ago, and yet he is still very much alive, and his name is equated with that of geometry itself. What has happened to him happens to every man whose name was equated with that of a thing; the thing is known but the man himself is forgotten. When I was a child, the table of multiplication was called the Table of Pythagoras, but the teacher did not tell us who Pythagoras was; perhaps she did not know it herself; she would have been

3

a very wise person if she did. Pythagoras was simply a common name to us like sandwich, mackintosh or macadam. Thus it was wrong to say that Euclid is very much alive today; geometry is but not he. His name is very often on our lips, but who was he? The purpose of my first lecture is to explain that, but no man ever lives in a social vacuum, and to bring him back to life we must, first of all, describe his environment. This is something important which many historians of science shamefully neglect; it is foolish to speak of great men of science without trying to explain their personality and their genius, neither of which can be understood outside of the social environment wherein they developed.

1. THE ALEXANDRIAN RENAISSANCE

In the first volume of my *History of Science,* I have described ancient science down to the end of Hellenic days. Euclid stands at the beginning of a new age, absolutely different in many respects from the preceding, and generally called the Hellenistic Age. The word Hellenistic is well chosen, it suggests Hellenism plus something else, foreign to it, Egyptian and oriental.

The break between those two ages, one of the greatest revolutions or discontinuities in history, was caused by Alexander the Great (IV-2 B.C.), who conquered a great part of the world within twelve years, from 334 to his death in 323 at the ripe age of thirty-three. As his armies were Greek, he carried Greek culture into the very heart of Asia; it has been said that he Hellenized Western Asia, but it could be said as well that he helped to orientalize Eastern Europe. Many cities were founded by him and bear a name derived from his, Alexandria, some as far East as Sogdiana beyond the Oxus, or India

Superior beyond the Indus. By far the most important was the one founded soon after his conquest of Egypt in 331.

The Greeks called that city Alexandreia hē pros Aigyptō (Latin, Alexandria ad Aegyptum) and rightly so, because it stood at the edge of Egypt and was very different from it. It is as if we said that Hong Kong is *near* China. The comparison is useful, because, just as in Hong Kong the overwhelming majority of the inhabitants are Chinese, we may assume that in Alexandria the majority were native Egyptians. The ruling class was Macedonian or Greek; as the city became more prosperous, it attracted a great diversity of foreigners, Ethiopians or Abyssinians and other Africans who came down the Nile; Asiatics, primarily Jews, but also Syrians, Persians, Arabs, Hindus. Alexandria soon became (and has remained throughout the ages) one of the most cosmopolitan cities of the world. Its harbor was and has remained the largest of the Eastern Mediterranean Sea.

This suggests another comparison, which I find very helpful, with New York. Alexandria's relationship to Athens in ancient times was comparable to New York's relationship to London. If one considers the speed of communication then and now, the distances, Alexandria-Athens and New York-London were about the same; New York was an offspring of Europe, just as much as Alexandria. Finally, its cosmopolitanism, and especially its Jewishness, make of it the American Alexandria. The main difference is that New York is essentially American, while Alexandria was definitely a Greek colony.

Alexander died in Babylon in the middle of June 323 and soon afterwards one of his closest companions, a Macedonian called Ptolemaios, son of Lagos,[1] became the governor or master of Egypt; in 304 he proclaimed himself king and founded the Ptolemaic dynasty, which lasted until 30 B.C.—for three centuries. Ptolemaios I Sōtēr must have been a man of considerable genius; not only was he the founder of a dynasty, but he was a patron of science and arts and wrote what was perhaps the best history of Alexander the Great. When he died in 283/2, he was succeeded by his son, Ptolemaios II Philadelphos, who ruled until 246 and completed his father's task. The Alexandrian Renaissance was mainly accomplished by these two kings within the first half of the third century; I introduced them both, because it is not always possible to separate their achievements.

In order to create the new civilization in Alexandria, they needed the help of other Greeks, not only soldiers and merchants but also intellectuals of various kinds, administrators, philosophers, teachers, poets, artists and men of science. Before dealing with Euclid, it is well to speak of some of them.

In the first place, we shall speak of the architects, for to build a new town in the Greek style such were needed. The Greeks were great town builders and did not allow the new cities to grow at random. The planning of Alexandria was intrusted by Alexander or more probably by the first Ptolemaios to Deinocratēs of Rhodes, who was perhaps the most

---

[1] The kings of that dynasty are often called Ptolemy; I prefer to use the original Greek form Ptolemaios (plural, Ptolemaioi), however, reserving the English form Ptolemy for a more illustrious person and one of far greater international significance, the astronomer Ptolemy (II-1), to whom my second lecture will be devoted. Hence, there will be no ambiguity; when I write Ptolemy, the astronomer is meant, while Ptolemaios is only a king.

eminent architect of his time. He it was who designed the new temple of Artemis at Ephesos, and he had conceived the idea of cutting one of the peaks of Mt. Athos in the shape of a gigantic statue of Alexander. The other architect, Sōstratos of Cnidos, built a lighthouse on a little island in the harbor. The island was called Pharos, and therefore the lighthouse received the same name.[2] It was the earliest lighthouse to be definitely known and described. A tower of about four hundred feet high, it could be seen over the plains or the sea from a long distance. It became so famous that it was generally listed as one of the seven wonders of the world.

The pharos was an outstanding symbol of Alexandrian prosperity; two institutions, the Museum and the Library, illustrated the greatness of Alexandrian culture.

There had been museums before in Greece, because a museum was simply a temple dedicated to the Muses, the nine goddesses of poetry, history and astronomy, but this museum was a new kind of institution which was so noteworthy that its name was preserved and has been incorporated into many languages. The meaning has changed, however, and museums all over the world are primarily buildings containing exhibitions of art, archaeology, natural history, etc. A certain amount of teaching and research is connected with the best of them; yet the Alexandrian exemplar was very different. If we had to describe its function in modern language, we would say that the Museum of Alexandria was primarily an institute for scientific research. It probably included dormitories for the men of science, their assistants and disciples, assembly

---

[2] Later the name was given to any lighthouse; it was transcribed with the same meaning in Latin and many Romance languages (L. *farus*, F. *phare*, It. and Sp. *fáro*, Port. *farol* or *pharol*, etc.) .

rooms, roofed colonnades for open-air study or discussion, laboratories, an observatory, botanical and zoological gardens. The Museum did not include all these features at the beginning, but like every institution, it grew in size and complexity as long as it was actually flourishing. Its scientific development owed much to its royal patrons and even more to Stratōn, who had been a pupil of Theophrastos. Stratōn was called to Alexandria by the first Ptolemaios (c. 300); we may call him the real founder of the Museum for he brought to it the intellectual atmosphere of the Lyceum, and it was thanks to him that it became not a school of poetry and eloquence, but an institute of scientific research. Stratōn was so deeply interested in the study of nature that he was nicknamed *ho physicos,* the physicist. Under the distant influence of Aristotle and the closer one of his own master, he realized that no progress is possible except on a scientific basis and he stressed the physical (vs. the metaphysical) tendencies of the Lyceum. He remained in Egypt many years, perhaps as many as twelve, or even more, being finally recalled to Athens when Theophrastos died in 288; he was appointed president or headmaster of the Lyceum (the third one) and directed it for about eighteen years (c. 288-c. 270). It is pleasant to think of the Museum being organized by an alumnus of the Lyceum, who later became its very head.

Much was done at the Museum during the first century of its existence. Mathematical investigations were led by Euclid, Eratosthenēs of Cyrēnē, who was first to measure the size of the earth and did it with remarkable precision, Apollōnios of Perga, who composed the first textbook on conics. Another contemporary giant, Archimēdēs, flourished in Syracuse, but he may have visited Alexandria and he was certainly influenced

8

by its mathematical school. The astronomical work was equally remarkable. Alexandria was an ideal place for astronomical syncretism; Greek, Egyptian and Babylonian ideas could mix freely, in the first place, because there were no established traditions, no "vested interests" of any kind, and secondly, because representatives of various races and creeds could and did actually meet. Astronomical observations were made by Aristyllos and Timocharis, and a little later by Conōn of Samos; the last-named used and discussed Babylonian observations of eclipses. Meanwhile, another Samosian, Aristarchos, was not only making observations of his own but defending theories of such boldness that he has been called "the Copernicus of antiquity."

The anatomical investigations carried through in the Museum were equally bold and fertile. Hērophilos of Chalcēdōn might be called the first scientific anatomist. He was flourishing under Ptolemaios Sōtēr, and it was probably he who devised the ambitious program of anatomical research, an elaborate survey of the human body on the basis of dissections. As this was done systematically for the first time, the men in charge were bound to make as many discoveries as an explorer who would happen to be the first to visit a new continent. Hērophilos was the main investigator and the catalogue of his observations is so long that it reads like the table of contents of an anatomical textbook. He obtained the help of another Greek, somewhat younger than himself, Erasistratos of Ceōs, who continued the anatomical survey and paid more attention to physiology. It was claimed by Celsus (I-1) and by church fathers who were eager to discredit pagan science that the Alexandrian anatomists were not satisfied with the dissection of dead bodies but obtained permission to dissect the bodies of living men, in order to have a better understanding of the functioning of the organs. The story as told by Celsus is plausible. We must bear in mind that the sensibility of the ancients was less keen than ours and that the Alexandrian anatomists were not hindered by religious or social restrictions. As far as we know, medicine was not included in the Museum program of research. It is possible that Stratōn or Hērophilos decided that medicine was too much of an art to reward purely scientific research; the time was not yet ripe for "experimental medicine."

Much of the work accomplished in mathematics, astronomy, mathematical geography, anatomy and physiology was analytical. With the exception of Euclid's *Elements*, the men of science wrote what we would call monographs, such as would be published today not in independent books but in journals. This reminds us of the cardinal fact that the Alexandrian Renaissance was a complete renaissance. At the beginning, I remarked that the discontinuity and the revolution following it were created by Alexander the Great. There is another aspect of this which deserves emphasis. A deeper discontinuity had been caused in the time of Alexander's youth by another Macedonian but a greater man than himself, his tutor, Aristotle. One ought to say Aristotle the Great and Alexander the Less. Aristotle was a philosopher, a man of science, an encyclopaedist who tried to organize and to unify the whole of knowledge. Considering his time and circumstances, his achievements are astounding and many of the results attained by him kept their validity for two thousand years. The conquests of Alexander were ephemeral; those of Aristotle were durable and exceedingly fertile. After the master's death, his

10

disciples in Athens and even more so those of Alexandria realized that the best way, nay, the only way of improving the Aristotelian synthesis was by means of analysis.

As opposed to the fourth century in Athens, the Alexandrian Renaissance was a period of analysis and research. This is an outstanding example of one of the fundamental rhythms of progress: analysis, synthesis, analysis, synthesis, and so on indefinitely.

Of the two leading institutions the one of greater interest to historians of science is the Museum. But it is probable that the Library was an integral part of the Museum (even as every research institute has a library of its own) ; both institutions were included in the royal city or enclosure; both were royal institutions, in the same way that they would be government ones today, for the king was the state, and everything done for the public good was done at the royal initiative and expense or not at all. The Museum and its Library were public utilities.

An elaborate study of the Library has recently been published by Dr. Parsons,[3] who has put together all the documents available, but in spite of his zeal and ingenuity, our knowledge of it is still very fragmentary. Many questions are still unanswerable. The first organizer as well as the first collector was almost certainly Dēmētrios of Phalēron, who worked hand in glove with the first king and was probably clever enough to give his royal patron the feeling of being the real creator. Dr. Parsons gives us a list of the "librarians" beginning with Dēmētrios and ending with the eighth one, Aristarchos of

[3] Edward Alexander Parsons, *The Alexandrian Library, Glory of the Hellenic World. Its Rise, Antiquities and Destruction* (New York, Elsevier, 1952; *Isis 43*, 286).

11

Samothracē (in 145 B.C.), which is very interesting in spite of the many conjectures which are implied. The main conclusion that one can draw from it is that the period of creative activity of the Library lasted only one and a half centuries (otherwise we would know the names of later librarians); this period was also that of greatest commercial prosperity. After the second century B.C., the Library declined and fell into somnolence. At the time of its climax, it had been exceedingly rich. It may have contained 400,000 "rolls." But it is impossible to be sure, not only because the sources are lacking but also because the counting of rolls and books is not as simple an operation, nor the total result as determined, as one might think. It was not by any means the earliest library, but it was by far the largest one of antiquity and found no equal perhaps until the tenth century when very large collections of books became available in the Muslim world, both East in Baghdād and West in Cordova.[4] By the middle of the third century, the Library of Alexandria was already so large that the creation of a new library, or call it "branch" library, was found to be necessary. This was the Serapeion, which earned some fame of its own, especially in Roman times.

The Library suffered many vicissitudes. It may have been damaged (or many books lost) in 48 B.C., when Caesar was obliged to set fire to the Egyptian fleet in the harbor nearby. A few years later, in 40, Anthony is said to have given to

---

[4] For the Baghdād libraries, see their catalogue, *Fihrist al-'ulūm,* written in 987 (see my *Introduction to the History of Science* [3 vols., Baltimore, Carnegie Institution of Washington, 1927-48] *1,* 662); the Cordova library was gathered mainly by the caliph al-Ḥakam II, who died in 976 (*Intro. 1,* 658). It is curious that these two libraries date from the same time (X-2).

Cleopatra the library of Pergamon, but did that really happen? At the time of the Jewish historian Joseph (I-2) both libraries were still very rich. Decadence was rapid during the second century and there is good reason for believing that many books (as well as other things) were taken to Rome. Under Aurelian (Emperor, 270-75) the Museum and the mother Library ceased to exist; the Serapeion then became the main Library and the last refuge of pagan culture. In 391, Theophilos (Bishop of Alexandria, 385-412), wishing to put an end to paganism, destroyed the Serapeion; it is possible, however, that the destruction was not complete and that many books could be saved in one way or another. Not a great many, however, if we believe Orosius' account of c. 416. When the Muslims sacked Alexandria in 646, it is claimed that they destroyed the Library; that can only mean that they destroyed the little that was left of it. The story of the great library, if it could be told with precision, would be a history of the decadence and fall of Alexandrian (pagan) culture. This cannot be done, but it is certain that the climax was long past before the age of Christ.

Let us return to its golden days. The Library was the main center of information for every department, but for the humanities it was much more than that: it was the brain and heart of every literary and historical study. The astronomers observed the heavens and measured the Earth, the anatomists dissected human bodies. But the primary materials of historians and philologists were in the library books and nowhere else.

The librarians had not as easy a task as their colleagues of today, who deal almost exclusively with printed books, each of which is a very tangible object. The first technical librarian,

Zēnodotos of Ephesos, had to identify the rolls and put together those which belonged together, for example, the rolls of the *Iliad* and *Odyssey*. He was, in fact, the first scientific editor of those epics. The same process had to be followed for all the rolls; they had to be investigated, one by one, identified, classified and finally edited as much as possible; it was necessary to establish the text of each author and to determine canons—the Homeric one, the Hippocratic, etc. In other words, Zēnodotos and his followers were not only librarians, but philologists. Callimachos of Cyrēnē, poet and scholar, came to Alexandria before the middle of the third century and was employed in making a catalogue of the library, the *Pinaces,* which was the earliest work of its kind.[5] It was very large, for it filled 120 rolls. Would that it had been preserved! Our knowledge of ancient literature, chiefly but not exclusively Greek, would have been much greater than it is. Indeed, a great many of the books which were available to Alexandrian scholars have long ceased to exist; we often know the names of the authors and the titles of the lost books; in some favorable cases, extracts have been transmitted to us in other books; in exceptional cases, the whole books have been preserved.

Many historians used the Library of Alexandria; one of the first to do so, perhaps, was the first king when he composed the life of Alexander. A curious case was that of Manethōn, who

---

[5] Some lists of Sumerian writings are considerably older but very short (see my *A History of Science: Ancient Science through the Golden Age of Greece* [Cambridge, Harvard University Press, 1952] *1,* 96). Whenever a large number of tablets was kept together, some kind of list may have proved necessary, but such lists were so rudimentary as compared with Callimachos' *catalogue raisonné* that the term catalogue as applied to them is figurative.

wrote Annals of Egypt in Greek on the basis of Egyptian documents (whether these existed in the Library or in Temples cannot be ascertained). The great geographer Eratosthenēs who was Librarian (the only man of science to hold that position, but he was also a distinguished man of letters) realized the essential need of historical research, scientific chronology. When one deals with a single country, say, Egypt, a precise dynastic history such as Manethōn had tried to produce may be sufficient, but when one has to study many countries, one must be able to correlate their national chronologies, and this is not possible unless one has a chronological frame applying to all of them. The first such frame had been imagined by the Sicilian Timaios, who suggested using the Olympic games as references. Those games had become international events in the Greek-speaking world and were of such importance that we may assume that foreigners would attend them occasionally; they occurred every fourth year from 776 on and hence might provide an international scale.[6] It is not clear whether Timaios was ever in touch with the historians of the Museum, and whether Eratosthenēs improved his invention. The Olympic scale was introduced too late (beginning of the third century B.C.) to remain long in use, because the rulers of the Western world replaced it by another scale (A.U.C., from the foundation of Rome in 753 B.C.), and it was completely superseded in the course of time by the Christian and the Muslim

[6] The numbering of the games began with those of 776, but many had occurred before. A list of the Olympic winners has been preserved by Eusebios (IV-1); it extends from 776 B.C. to 217 A.D., almost a millenium (994 years). The Olympic era was used only by a few scholars, such as Polybios (II-1 B.C.) and Castōr of Rhodos (I-1 B.C.); the Greek cities continued to date events with reference to their own magistrates and, moreover, they used different calendars.

eras.[7] The point to bear in mind is that scientific chronology began in Alexandria; Eratosthenēs' interest in it is comparable to his interest in geographical coordinates—which are of the same necessity in a two-dimensional continuum (a spherical surface) as fixed dates along the line of time.

The identification of texts and their establishment opened the door to every branch of philology, in the first place, grammar. Not only was grammar needed to determine the sense of a text without ambiguity but in a polyglot city like Alexandria it became necessary for the teaching of Greek to foreigners. Erastosthenēs was the first man to call himself philologist (philologos). Aristophanēs of Byzantion (II-1 B.C.) and Aristarchos of Samothracē (II-1 B.C.) were the first grammarians *stricto sensu*.[8] Both were librarians of the Museum, Aristophanēs from 195 to 180, Aristarchos from c. 160 to 143 (or 131?).[9] The earliest Greek grammar extant was composed

---

[7] To summarize:
    Ol. 1.1 = 776 B.C.
    Ol. 2.1 = 772 B.C.
    U.C. 1 = 753 B.C. = Ol. 6.4.
    B.C. 1 = 753 U.C. = Ol. 194.4.
    A.D. 1 = 754 U.C. = Ol. 195.1.
To make matters worse, a new Olympiad era was introduced by Hadrian; it began when he dedicated the Olympieion in Athens: *New* Ol. 1 = Ol. 227.3 = U.C. 884 = A.D. 131.

[8] Philology and in particular grammar are bound to occur when different languages are used simultaneously, e.g., in the Mesopotamian and Anatolian world (*History of Science 1,* 67). In Greece proper, it developed relatively late, because the language spoken in educated circles was relatively pure and homogeneous. Nevertheless, grammar was a child of logic and some grammatical functions were bound to be discovered as soon as one attempted the logical analysis of any sentence (*History of Science 1,* 257, 579, 602).

[9] According to Parsons' list (p. 60), they were the sixth and eighth

by another Alexandrian, Dionysios Thrax (II-2 B.C.). The masterpieces of Greek literature were written before 300 B.C., the first grammar almost two centuries later. The fact that the Hellenistic age witnessed the development of grammar as well as the development of anatomy is a natural coincidence. They were the fruits of the same analytical and scientific mentality, applied in the first place to the language and, in the second, to the body of man.

Euclid has long been waiting for us, and it is high time that we return to him; yet, a few words should be said of the most astonishing philological achievement of his time, the *Septuagint*.

The name will explain itself in a moment. According to the story told in Greek by the Jew Aristeas,[10] Dēmētrios of Phalēron explained to King Ptolemaios II the need for translating the Tōrāh into Greek. It is a fact that the large and influential Jewish colony of Alexandria was losing its command of the Hebrew language; on the other hand, a Greek version of the Tōrāh might interest some of the Gentiles. The king sent two ambassadors to the High Priest Eleazar in Jerusalem, asking for Hebrew rolls of the Old Testament and for six representatives of each tribe. The royal demand was obeyed and seventy-two Jewish scholars were soon established in the Pharos island and started their translation of the Holy Scriptures. The translation might have been called *Septuaginta duo*, but the second word was dropped. Aristeas' story was

director-librarians, the eighth being the last. The list is tentative and suggests many objections, yet it is useful.

[10] For more details, see the excellent edition and translation of the letter of Aristeas to Philocratēs by Moses Hadas (New York, Harper, 1951; *Isis 43*, 287-88).

embellished by later writers; the details of it do not matter. The Tōrāh was actually translated into Greek during the third century. Other books of the Old Testament were translated later, many of them in the second century B.C., the last one, *Qoheleth* (*Ecclēsiastēs*) not until about 100 A.D.[11]

This Greek translation of the Old Testament is very important, because it was made upon the basis of a Hebrew text more ancient than the Hebrew text which has been transmitted to us.[12] Hence, any student of the Old Testament must know Greek as well as Hebrew.

---

[11] The original text of *Qoheleth* was produced very late, say, in the period 250-168. This accounts for the exceptional lateness of its translation. It was probably prepared c. 130 by Aquila, the Christianized disciple of R. Akiba ben Joseph. It is not really a part of the *Septuagint* but of the Version of Aquila (*Intro. 1*, 291). Practically the whole of the O.T. was translated into Greek before the Christian era, and the name *Septuagint* should be restricted to these pre-Christian versions.

[12] It was believed that the Hebrew scrolls discovered by Beduins in 1947 in a cave along the western shore of the Dead Sea included earlier readings than those reproduced in the Hebrew Bible. Isaiah and Habakkuk scrolls and other fragments already deciphered do not sustain that belief, for they do not seem to have a closer connection with the *Septuagint* text than the *Masoretic* text has. The dating of those scrolls is very difficult, but the arguments from paleography, archeology, radio-carbon testing, and historical background would appear to fix the Mishnaic period at least as well as any others. If more precision were desired, one might perhaps say that the scrolls date from the century following the destruction of the Second Temple and of the Jewish State in 70 A.D. Incidentally, the radio-carbon dating is very inconclusive, because according to that method the piece of linen used for wrapping dates from the period 33 A.D. $\pm$ 200. There is already an abundant literature on the many problems raised by those scrolls. For general information, see Harold Henry Rowley, *The Zadokite Fragments and the Dead Sea Scrolls* (Oxford, Blackwell, 1952). The writing of this footnote was made possible by the kindness of Abraham A. Neuman, president of Dropsie College in Philadelphia (letter dated 30 Nov., 1953).

The ancient Greeks had hardly paid any attention to the queer people living in Palestine so near to their own colonies. In Hellenistic times, this situation was reversed, because Greeks and Jews were sharing the same environment in Egypt. This was carried so far that Hellenistic scholars actually helped the tradition of the Hebrew Scriptures.

2. EUCLID

And now, at last, let us consider Euclid[13] himself. We can visualize very clearly his environment, the people and things surrounding him, but who was he himself?

Unfortunately, our knowledge of him is very limited. This is not an exceptional case. Mankind remembers the tyrants, the successful politicians, the men of wealth, but it forgets its true benefactors. How much do we know about Shakespeare? I shall tell you all we know about Euclid, and that will not take very long.

The places and dates of birth and death are unknown. He was probably educated in Athens and, if so, received his mathematical training at the Academy; he flourished in Alexandria under the first Ptolemaios and possibly under the second. Two anecdotes help to reveal his personality. It is said that the king (Ptolemaios I) asked him "if there was in geometry any shorter way than that of the *Elements,* and he answered that there was no royal road to geometry." This is an excellent story, which may not be true as far as Euclid is concerned but has an eternal validity. Mathematics is "no respecter of

[13] His name reads Eucleidēs, but it would be pedantic to use it instead of Euclid, a proper name which has attained the dignity of a common name in our language. It is for the same reason (fear of pedantry) that I shall write Ptolemy when speaking of the astronomer.

19

persons." The other anecdote is equally good. "Someone who had begun to read geometry with Euclid when he had learned the first theorem asked him, 'But what shall I get by learning these things?' Euclid called his slave and said, 'Give him an obol, since he must gain out of what he learns.' "

Both anecdotes are recorded relatively late, the first by Proclos, the second by Stobaios, both of whom lived in the second half of the fifth century; they are plausible enough and traditions of that homely kind would be tenacious.

Euclid was not officially connected with the Museum; otherwise the fact would have been recorded. But if he flourished in Alexandria, he was necessarily acquainted with the Museum and the Library. As a pure mathematician, however, he did not need any laboratory and the manuscripts in his own possession might have made him independent of the Library. The number of manuscripts which he needed was not considerable; a good student might easily copy the needed texts during his school years. A mathematician does not need many collaborators; like the poet, he does his best work alone, very quietly. On the other hand, he may have been teaching a few disciples; this would have been natural and is confirmed by Pappos' remark that Apollōnios of Perga (III-2 B.C.) was trained in Alexandria by Euclid's pupils.

Euclid himself was so little known that he was confused for a considerable time with the philosopher, Euclid of Megara,[14] who had been one of Sōcratēs' disciples (one of the

[14] I failed to devote a special note to him in my *Introduction*; he is simply referred to in a footnote (*1*, 153); thus was an old tradition reversed. For a long time, Euclid of Alexandria was overshadowed by Euclid of Megara; now the latter tends to be forgotten, because he is eclipsed by the only Euclid whom everybody knows, the mathematician.

faithful who attended the master's death), a friend of Plato's and the founder of a philosophical school in Megara. The confusion began very early and was confirmed by the early printers until late in the sixteenth century. The first to correct the error in an Euclidean edition was Federigo Commandino in his Latin translation (Pesaro, 1572).

Euclid is thus like Homer. As everybody knows the *Iliad* and the *Odyssey,* so does everybody know the *Elements.* Who is Homer? He is the author of the *Iliad.* Who is Euclid? He is the author of the *Elements.*

The *Elements* is the earliest textbook on geometry which has come down to us. Its importance was soon realized and thus the text has been transmitted to us in its integrity. It is divided into thirteen books, which may be described briefly as follows:

Books I to VI: Plane geometry. Book I is, of course, fundamental; it includes the definitions and postulates and deals with triangles, parallels, parallelograms, etc. The contents of Book II might be called "geometrical algebra." Book III: Geometry of the circle. Book IV: Regular polygons. Book V: New theory of proportion applied to incommensurable as well as commensurable quantities. Book VI: Applications of the theory to plane geometry.

Books VII to X: Arithmetic, theory of numbers. Numbers of many kinds, primes or prime to one another, least common multiples, numbers in geometrical progression, etc. Book X, which is Euclid's masterpiece, is devoted to irrational lines, all the lines which can be represented by an expression, such as

$$\sqrt{(\sqrt{a} \pm \sqrt{b})}$$

wherein a and b are commensurable lines.

Books XI-XIII: Solid geometry. Book XI is very much like Books I and VI extended to a third dimension. Book XII applies the method of exhaustion to the measurement of circles, spheres, pyramids, etc. Book XIII deals with regular solids.

Plato's fantastic speculations had raised the theory of regular polyhedra to a high level of significance. Hence, a good knowledge of the "Platonic bodies"[15] was considered by many good people as the crown of geometry. Proclos (V-2) suggested that Euclid was a Platonist and that he had built his geometrical monument for the purpose of explaining the Platonic figures. That is obviously wrong. Euclid may have been a Platonist, of course, but he may have preferred another philosophy or he may have carefully avoided philosophical implications. The theory of regular polyhedra is the natural culmination of solid geometry and hence the *Elements* could not but end with it.

It is not surprising, however, that the early geometers who tried to continue the Euclidean efforts devoted special attention to the regular solids. Whatever Euclid may have thought of these solids "beyond mathematics" they were, especially for the neo-Platonists, the most fascinating items in geometry. Thanks to them, geometry obtained a cosmical meaning and a theological value.

Two more books dealing with the regular solids were added to the *Elements,* called books XIV and XV and included in many editions and translations, manuscript or printed. The so-called "Book XIV" was composed by Hypsiclēs of Alexandria at the beginning of the second century B.C. and is a

---

[15] For a discussion of the regular polyhedra and of the Platonic aberrations relative to them, see my *History of Science* (*1,* 438-39) .

work of outstanding merit; the other treatise "Book XV" is of
a much later time and inferior in quality; it was written by a
pupil of Isidōros of Milētos (the architect of Hagia Sophia,
c. 532).

To return to Euclid and especially to his main work, the
thirteen books of the *Elements,* when judging him, we should
avoid two opposite mistakes which have been made repeatedly.
The first is to speak of him as if he were the originator, the
father of geometry. As I have already explained apropos of
Hippocratēs, the so-called "father of medicine," there are no
unbegotten fathers except Our Father in heaven. If we take
Egyptian and Babylonian efforts into account, as we should,
Euclid's *Elements* is the climax of more than a thousand years.
One might object that Euclid deserves to be called the father
of geometry for another reason. Granted that many discoveries were made before him, he was the first to build a
synthesis of all the knowledge obtained by others and himself
and to put all the known propositions in a strong logical order.
That statement is not absolutely true. Propositions had been
proved before Euclid and chains of propositions established;
moreover, "Elements" had been composed before him by Hippocratēs of Chios (V B.C.), by Leōn (IV-1 B.C.), and finally
by Theudios of Magnēsia (IV-2 B.C.). Theudios' treatise, with
which Euclid was certainly familiar, had been prepared for
the Academy, and it is probable that a similar one was in use
in the Lyceum. At any rate, Aristotle knew Eudoxos' theory
of proportion and the method of exhaustion, which Euclid
expanded in Books V, VI and XII of the *Elements.* In short,
whether you consider particular theorems or methods or the
arrangement of the *Elements,* Euclid was seldom a complete

innovator; he did much better and on a larger scale what other geometers had done before him.

The opposite mistake is to consider Euclid as a "textbook maker" who invented nothing and simply put together in better order the discoveries of other people. It is clear that a schoolmaster preparing today an elementary book of geometry can hardly be considered a creative mathematician; he is a textbook maker (not a dishonorable calling, even if the purpose is more often than not purely meretricious), but Euclid was not.

A good many propositions in the *Elements* can be ascribed to earlier geometers, but we may assume that those which cannot be ascribed to others were discovered by Euclid himself; and their number is considerable. As to the arrangement, it is safe to assume that it is to a large extent Euclid's own. He created a monument which is as marvelous in its symmetry, inner beauty and clearness as the Parthenōn, but incomparably more complex and more durable.

A full proof of this bold statement cannot be given in a few paragraphs or in a few pages. To appreciate the richness and greatness of the *Elements* one must study them in a well annotated translation like Heath's. It is not possible to do more, here and now, than emphasize a few points. Consider Book I, explaining first principles, definitions, postulates, axioms, theorems and problems. It is possible to do better at present, but it is almost unbelievable that anybody could have done as well twenty-two centuries ago. The most amazing part of Book I is Euclid's choice of postulates. Aristotle was, of course, Euclid's teacher in such matters; he had devoted much attention to mathematical principles, had shown the unavoidability of postulates and the need for reducing them to a minimum;[16] yet, the choice of postulates was Euclid's.

In particular, the choice of postulate 5 is, perhaps, his greatest achievement, the one which has done more than any other to immortalize the word "Euclidean." Let us quote it verbatim:[17]

> . . . if a straight line falling on two straight lines make the interior angles on the same side less than two right angles, the two straight lines if produced indefinitely meet on that side on which the angles are less than two right angles."

A person of average intelligence would say that the proposition is evident and needs no proof; a better mathematician would realize the need of a proof and attempt to give it; it required extraordinary genius to realize that a proof was needed yet impossible. There was no way out, then, from Euclid's point of view, but to accept it as a postulate and go ahead.

The best way to measure Euclid's genius as evidenced by this momentous decision is to examine the consequences of it. The first consequence, as far as Euclid was immediately concerned, was the admirable concatenation of his *Elements*. The second was the endless attempts which mathematicians made to correct him; the first to make them were Greeks, like Ptolemy (II-1) and Proclos (V-2); then Muslims, chiefly the Persian, Naṣīr al-dīn al-Ṭūsī (XIII-2), the Jew, Levi ben Gerson (XIV-1), and finally "modern" mathematicians, like John

---

[16] Aristotle's views can be read in Heath's *Euclid* (*1*, 117 ff., 1926) or in his posthumous book, *Mathematics in Aristotle* (Oxford, Clarendon Press, 1949; *Isis 41*, 329).

[17] For the Greek text and a much fuller discussion of it than can be given here, see Heath's *Euclid* (*1*, 202-20). See also Roberto Bonola, *Non-Euclidean Geometry* (Chicago, 1912; *Horus* 154).

Wallis (1616-1703), the Jesuit father, Gerolamo Saccheri (1667-1733), of San Remo in his *Euclides ab omni naevo vindicatus* (1733), the Swiss,[18] Johann Heinrich Lambert (1728-77), and the Frenchman, Adrien Marie Legendre (1752-1833). The list could be lengthened considerably, but these names suffice, because they are the names of illustrious mathematicians representing many countries and many ages, down to the middle of the last century. The third consequence is illustrated by the list of alternatives to the fifth postulate. Some bright men thought that they could rid themselves of the postulate and succeeded in doing so, but at the cost of introducing another one (explicit or implicit) equivalent to it. For example,

> "If a straight line intersects one of two parallels, it will intersect the other also." (Proclos)
> "Given any figure there exists a figure similar to it of any size." (John Wallis)
> "Through a given point only one parallel can be drawn to a given straight line." (John Playfair)
> "There exists a triangle in which the sum of the three angles is equal to two right angles." (Legendre)
> "Given any three points not in a straight line there exists a circle passing through them." (Legendre)
> "If I could prove that a rectilinear triangle is possible the content of which is greater than any given area, I would be in a position to prove perfectly rigorously the whole of geometry." (Gauss, 1799).

All these men proved that the fifth postulate is not necessary if one accepts another postulate rendering the same ser-

[18] Yes, Swiss (*Isis 40*, 139).

vice. The acceptance of any of those alternatives (those quoted above and many others) would, however, increase the difficulty of geometrical teaching; the use of some of them would seem very artificial and would discourage young students. It is clear that a simple exposition is preferable to one which is more difficult; the setting up of avoidable hurdles would prove the teacher's cleverness and his lack of common sense. Thanks to his genius, Euclid saw the necessity of this postulate and selected intuitively the simplest form of it. There were also many mathematicians who were so blind that they rejected the fifth postulate without realizing that another was taking its place. They kicked one postulate out of the door and another came in through the window without their being aware of it!

The fourth consequence, and the most remarkable, was the creation of non-Euclidean geometries. The initiators have already been named, Saccheri, Lambert, Gauss. Inasmuch as the fifth postulate cannot be proved, we are not obliged to accept it, and if so, let us deliberately reject it. The first to build a new geometry on an opposite postulate was a Russian, Nikolai Ivanovich Lobachevskii (1793-1850), who assumed that through a given point more than one parallel can be drawn to a given straight line or that the sum of the angles of a triangle is less than two right angles. The discovery of a non-Euclidean geometry was made at about the same time by a Transylvanian, János Bólyai (1802-60). Sometime later, another geometry was outlined by a German, Bernhard Riemann (1826-66), who was not acquainted with the writings of Lobachevskii and Bólyai and made radically new assumptions. In Riemann's geometry, there are no parallel lines and the sum of the angles of a triangle is greater than two right angles. The great mathematical teacher Felix Klein (1847-1925) showed the relationship of all those geometries. Euclid's geometry refers to a surface of zero curvature, in between Riemann's geometry on a surface of positive curvature (like the sphere) and Lobachevskii's applying to a surface of negative curvature. To put it more briefly, he called the Euclid geometry parabolic, because it is the limit of elliptic (Riemann's) geometry on one side and of the hyperbolic (Lobachevskii's) geometry on the other.

It would be foolish to give credit to Euclid for pangeometrical conceptions; the idea of a geometry different from the common-sense one never occurred to his mind. Yet, when he stated the fifth postulate, he stood at the parting of the ways. His subconscious prescience is astounding. There is nothing comparable to it in the whole history of science.

It would be unwise to claim too much for Euclid. The fact that he put at the beginning of the *Elements* a relatively small number of postulates is very remarkable, especially when one considers the early date, say, 300 B.C., but he could not fathom the depths of postulational thinking any more than he could fathom those of non-Euclidian geometry. Yet he was the distant forerunner of David Hilbert (1862-1911) even as he was Lobachevskii's spiritual ancestor.[19]

Enough has been said of Euclid the geometer, but one must not overlook other aspects of his genius as mathematician and physicist. To begin with, the *Elements* does not deal

---

[19] For details, see Florian Cajori, *History of Mathematics* (2nd ed., 326-28, 1919); Cassius Jackson Keyser, *The Rational and the Superrational* (pp. 136-44, New York, Scripta Mathematica, 1952; *Isis 44*, 171).

simply with geometry but also with algebra and the theory of numbers.

Book II might be called a treatise on geometrical algebra. Algebraical problems are stated in geometrical terms and solved by geometrical methods. For example, the product of two numbers a, b is represented by the rectangle whose sides have the lengths a and b; the extraction of a square root is reduced to the finding of a square equal to a given rectangle, etc. The distributive and commutative laws of algebra are proved geometrically. Various identities, even complicated ones, are presented by Euclid in a purely geometrical form. E.g.,

$$a^2 + b^2 = 2\left\{\left(\frac{a+b}{2}\right)^2 + \left(\frac{a+b}{2} - b\right)^2\right\}$$

$$\text{or } (a + b)^2 + (b - a)^2 = 2(a^2 + b^2)$$

This might seem to be a step backward as compared with the methods of Babylonian algebra, and one wonders how that could happen. It is highly probable that the clumsy symbolism of Greek numeration was the fundamental cause of that regression; it was easier to handle lines than Greek numbers!

At any rate, Babylonian algebraists were not acquainted with irrational quantities, while Book X of the *Elements* (the largest of the thirteen books, even larger than Book I) is devoted exclusively to them. Here again, Euclid was building on older foundations, but this time the foundations were purely Greek. We may believe the story ascribing recognition of irrational quantitites to early Pythagoreans, and Plato's friend Theaitētos (IV-1 B.C.) gave a comprehensive theory of them as well as of the five regular solids. There is no better

29

illustration of the Greek mathematical genius (as opposed to the Babyonian one) than the theory of irrationals as explained by Hippasos of Metapontion, Theodōros of Cyrēnē, Theaitētos of Athens and finally by Euclid.[20] It is impossible to say just how much of Book X was created by Theaitētos and how much by Euclid himself. We have no choice but to consider that book as an essential part of the *Elements*, irrespective of its origin. It is divided into three parts, each of which is preceded by a group of definitions. A number of propositions deal with surds in general, but the bulk of the book investigates the complex irrationals which we would represent by the symbols

$$\sqrt{(\sqrt{a} \pm \sqrt{b})}$$

wherein *a* and *b* are commensurable quantities. These irrationals are divided into twenty-five species, each of which is discussed separately. As Euclid did not use algebraical symbols, he adopted geometrical representations for these quantities and his discussion of them was geometrical. Book X was much admired, especially by Arabic mathematicians; it remains a great achievement but is practically obsolete, for such discussions are futile from the point of view of modern algebra.

Books VII to IX of the *Elements* might be called the first treatise on the theory of numbers, one of the most abstruse branches of the mathematical tree. It would be impossible to summarize their contents, for the summary would be almost

[20] For Hippasos', Theodōros', and Theaitētos' contributions see my *History of Science* (pp. 282-85, 437).

meaningless unless it covered a good many pages.[21] Let me just say that Book VII begins with a list of twenty-two definitions, which are comparable to the geometrical definitions placed at the beginning of Book I. Euclid sets forth a series of proportions concerning the divisibility of numbers, even and odd numbers, squares and cubes, prime and perfect numbers, etc.

Let us give two examples. In IX, 36 he proves that if $p = 1 + 2 + \ldots + 2^n$ is prime, $2^n p$ is perfect (that is, equal to the sum of its divisors). In IX, 20 we are given an excellent demonstration that the number of prime numbers is infinite.

The demonstration is so simple and our intuitive feeling *ad hoc* so strong that one would readily accept other propositions of the same kind. For example, there are many prime pairs, that is, prime numbers packed as closely as possible ($2n + 1$, $2n + 3$, both primes, e.g., 11, 13; 17, 19; 41, 43). As one proceeds in the series of numbers, prime pairs become rarer and rarer, yet one can hardly escape the feeling that the number of prime pairs is infinite. The proof of that is so difficult, however, that it has not yet been completed.[22]

In this field again, Euclid was an outstanding innovator, and the few mathematicians of our own days who are trying to cultivate it recognize him as their master.

---

[21] The Greek text of Books VII to IX covers 116 pages in Heiberg's edition (*2*, Leipzig, 1884) and the English translation with notes, 150 pages in Heath's second volume.

[22] Charles N. Moore offered a proof in 1944, but that proof was shown to be insufficient (*Horus* 62). The incredible complexity of the theory of numbers can be appreciated by looking at its *History* written by Leonard Eugene Dickson (3 vols., Carnegie Institution, 1919-23; *Isis 3*, 446-48; *4*, 107-08; *6*, 96-98). For prime pairs, see Dickson, *1*, 353, 425, 438.

Thus far, we have spoken only of the *Elements,* but Euclid
wrote many other works, some of which are lost; these works
deal not only with geometry but also with astronomy, physics,
and music. The genuineness of some of those treatises is
doubtful. For example, two treatises on optics are ascribed to
him, the *Optics* and the *Catoptrics.*[23] The first is genuine, the
second probably apocryphal. We have the text of the *Optics,*
and we have also a review of both treatises by Theōn of Alexandria (IV-2). The *Optics* begins with definitions or rather
assumptions, derived from the Pythagorean theory that the
rays of light are straight lines and proceed from the eye. Euclid
then explains problems of perspective. The *Catoptrics* deals
with mirrors and sets forth the law of reflection. It is a
remarkable chapter of mathematical physics which remained
almost alone of its kind for a very long period of time, but
does it date from the third century B.C., or is it later, much
later?

The tradition concerned with the fifth postulate has already been referred to; it can be traced from the time of the
Elements to our own. That is only a small part of it, however.
The Euclidean tradition, even if restricted to mathematics, is
remarkable for its continuity and the greatness of many of its
bearers. The ancient tradition includes such men as Pappos
(III-2) , Theōn of Alexandria (IV-2) , Proclos (V-2), Marinos of

[23] French translation by Paul Ver Eecke, *L'Optique et la Catoptrique*
(Bruges, 1938; *Isis 30,* 520-21). This includes French versions of the
Catoptrics and of the two texts of the *Optics,* the original one and the
ene edited by Theōn of Alexandria (IV-2). English translation of the
original text of the *Optics* by Harry Edwin Burton (*Journal of the Optical
Society of America 35* [1945], 357-72).

Sichem (V-2), Simplicios (VI-1). It was wholly Greek. Some Western scholars, such as Censorinus (III-1) and Boethius (VI-1), translated parts of the *Elements* from Greek into Latin, but very little remains of their efforts and one cannot speak of any complete translation, or of any one covering a large part of the *Elements*. There is much worse to be said; various manuscripts circulated in the West until as late as the twelfth century which contained only the propositions of Euclid without demonstrations.[24] The story was spread that Euclid himself had given no proofs and that these had been supplied only seven centuries later by Theōn of Alexandria (IV-2). One could not find a better example of incomprehension, for if Euclid had not known the proofs of his theorems he would not have been able to put them in a logical order. That order is the very essence and the greatness of the *Elements,* but medieval scholars did not see it, or at least did not see it until their eyes had been opened by Muslim commentators.

The Muslim study of Euclid was begun by al-Kindī (IX-1), if not before (al-Kindī's interest, however, was centered upon the optics, and in mathematics it extended to non-Euclidean topics such as Hindu numerals), and Muḥammad ibn Mūsā (IX-1). The *Elements* were first translated into Arabic by al-Ḥajjāj ibn Yūsuf (IX-1); he made a first translation for Hārūn al-Rashīd (caliph, 786-809), then revised it for al-Ma'mūn (caliph, 813-33). During the 250 years which followed, the Muslim mathematicians kept very close to Euclid, the algebraist as well as the geometer, and published other translations and many commentaries. Before the end of the ninth century, Euclid was translated and discussed in Arabic

[24] Greek and Latin editions of the propositions only, without proofs, were printed from 1547 to as late as 1587.

33

by al-Māhānī, al-Nairīzī, Thābit ibn Qurra, Isḥāq ibn Ḥunain, Qusṭā ibn Lūqā. A great step forward was made in the first quarter of the tenth century by Abū 'Uthmān Sa'īd ibn Ya'qūb al-Dimishqī, who translated Book X with Pappos' commentary (the Greek of which is lost) .[25] This translation increased Arabic interest in the contents of Book X (classification of incommensurable lines), as witnessed by the new translation of Naẓīf ibn Yumn (X-2), a Christian priest, and by the commentaries of Abū Ja'far al-Khāzin (X-2) and Muḥammad ibn 'Abd al-Bāqī al-Baghdādī (XI-2). My Arabic list is long yet very incomplete, because we must assume that every Arabic mathematician of this age was acquainted with the *Elements* and discussed Euclid. For example, Abū-l-Wafā' (X-2) is said to have written a commentary on Euclid which is lost.

We may now interrupt the Arabic story and return to the West. Western efforts to translate the *Elements* directly from Greek into Latin had been ineffective; it is probable that their knowledge of Greek diminished and dwindled almost to nothing at the very time when their interest in Euclid was increasing. Translators from the Arabic were beginning to appear and these were bound to come across Euclidean manuscripts. Efforts to Latinize these were made by Hermann the Dalmatian (XII-1), John O'Creat (XII-1), and Gerard of Cremona (XII-2), but there is no reason to believe that the translation was completed, except by Adelard of Bath (XII-1).[26] However, the Latin climate was not so favorable to

[25] The Arabic text of Abū 'Uthmān was edited and Englished by William Thomson, with mathematical introduction by Gustav Junge (*Harvard Semitic Series 8,* Cambridge, 1930; *Isis 16,* 132-36).

[26] The story is simplified for the sake of brevity; for details, see Marshall Clagett, "The medieval Latin translations from the Arabic of the *Elements*

geometrical research in the twelfth century as the Arabic climate had proved to be from the ninth century on. Indeed, we
have to wait until the beginning of the thirteenth century to
witness a Latin revival of the Euclidean genius, and we owe
that revival to Leonardo of Pisa (XIII-1), better known under
the name of Fibonacci. In his *Practica geometriae,* written in
1220, Fibonacci did not continue the *Elements,* however, but
another Euclidean work on the *Divisions of figures,* which is
lost.[27]

In the meanwhile, the Hebrew tradition was begun by
Judah ben Solomon ha-Kohen (XIII-1) and continued by
Moses ibn Tibbon (XIII-2), Jacob ben Maḥir ibn Tibbon
(XIII-2), and Levi ben Gerson (XIV-1). The Syriac tradition
was illustrated by Abū-l-Faraj, called Barhebraeus (XIII-2),
who lectured on Euclid at the observatory of Marāgha in 1268;
unfortunately, the beginning of the Syriac tradition was also
the end of it, because Abū-l-Faraj was the last Syriac writer
of importance; after his death, Syriac was gradually replaced
by Arabic.

The golden age of Arabic science was also on the wane,
though there remained a few illustrious Euclidians in the
thirteenth century, like Qaiṣar ibn abī-l-Qāsim (XIII-1), Ibn
al-Lubūdī (XIII-1), Naṣīr al-dīn al-Ṭūsī (XIII-2), Muḥyī al-dīn
al-Maghribī (XIII-2), Quṭb al-dīn al-Shīrāzī (XIII-2), and even
some in the fourteenth century. We may overlook the late Mus-

with special empasis on the versions of Adelard of Bath" (*Isis 44,* 16-42,
1953).

[27] The text of that little treatise *peri diaireseōn* was restored as far as
possible by Raymond Clare Archibald on the basis of Leonardo's *Practica*
and of an Arabic translation (*Intro. 1,* 154-55).

lim and Jewish mathematicians, however, for the main river was now flowing in the West.

Adelard's Latin text was revised by Giovanni Campano (XIII-2) and Campano's revision was immortalized in the earliest printed edition of the *Elements* (Venice, 1482). The first edition of the Greek text was printed in Basel, 1533, and the princeps of the Arabic text, as edited by Nasīr al-dīn al-Ṭūsī, was published in Rome in 1594.

The rest of the story need not be told here. The list of Euclidean editions which began in 1482 and is not ended yet is immense, and the history of the Euclidean tradition is an essential part of the history of geometry.

As far as elementary geometry is concerned, the *Elements* of Euclid is the only example of a textbook which has remained serviceable until our own days. Twenty-two centuries of changes, wars, revolutions, catastrophies of every kind, yet it still is possible and profitable to study geometry in Euclid!

3. BIBLIOGRAPHY OF EUCLID

Standard edition of the Greek text of all the works, with Latin versions, *Euclidis opera omnia* ediderunt J. L. Heiberg et H. Menge (8 vols., Leipzig, 1883-1916; supplement 1899).

Sir Thomas L. Heath. *Euclid's Elements in English* (3 vols., Cambridge, 1908), revised edition (3 vols., 1926; *Isis 10*, 60-62).

Charles Thomas-Stanford. *Early Editions of Euclid's Elements* (64 pp., 13 pl., London, 1926; *Isis 10*, 59-60).

PTOLEMY AND HIS TIME

(second century A.D.)

1. THE LONG DURATION AND COMPLEXITY OF ANCIENT SCIENCE

IGNORANT people think of "antiquity" or of the "Middle Ages" as if each of these periods were something homogeneous and unchanging, and they would put everything concerning ancient science (or medieval science) in a single box, just as if all these things were of the selfsame kind. That is very silly. The one thing which one might concede is that the change is faster now than it was in the past, but much of the increasing speed is superficial.

What we call classical antiquity, if we count it from Homer to Damascios, is a period of about fourteen centuries; if we count the length of American civilization in the same way (that is, leaving out, in both cases, the prehistoric times which are ageless), it has lasted about four centuries. Thus, the first of these periods is more than thrice longer than the second. And yet should one put the whole of American culture in a single bag, as if the whole of it were the same kind of biscuit? Certainly not.

There was incredible variety in ancient times, even within a single century, but there were also traditions which continued across the ages and are very helpful to us as guiding threads. For example, from Euclid's time on, there appeared in each century some mathematicians who continued Euclid's ideas or discussed them.

By the second century after Christ more than three centuries had elapsed since the beginning of the Hellenistic Age, and the world was exceedingly different from what it had been. The difference was not due so much to Christianity, which was still unfelt except by a small minority of people, and remained inoperative as an influence. The philosophical climate continued to be dominated by Stoïcism. The political world, however, was absolutely different.

2. THE ROMAN WORLD IN THE SECOND CENTURY

Let us consider a little more closely the world in which Ptolemy lived. It is probable that he was born in Egypt and flourished in Alexandria, but Egypt had been a Roman province since 30 B.C. The Greek chaos and the wars between Alexander's successors had been finally ended by Roman power. That new world was very imperfect in many ways but, for the first time in many centuries, there was a modicum of international order, law and peace. The second century was the end of the golden age of the Roman empire; it was de-

cidedly the golden age of Roman science, but the best of
Roman science was really Greek.

It was Ptolemy's privilege to live under some of the best
emperors, the Spaniard Trajan (ruled 98-117), who built roads,
libraries, bridges across the Danube and the Tagus; Hadrian
(ruled 117-38), also a great builder in Athens, Rome and
Tivoli; Antoninus Pius (ruled 138-61) and, perhaps, Marcus
Aurelius (ruled 161-80); these last two, not only great emperors, but good men. When one speaks of "pax romana," one
has in mind chiefly the forty-four years covered by the rules
of Hadrian and Antoninus, and apropos of the rules of
Antoninus and Marcus Aurelius, a stretch of almost equal
duration, Gibbon declared: "Their united reigns are possibly
the only period of history in which the happiness of a great
people was the sole object of government."[1]

The most significant thing about the Roman empire, from
the intellectual point of view, was its bilingualism. Every
educated man in the West was supposed to know two languages, Greek as well as Latin. By this time, the second century
after Christ, the golden age of Latin literature was already
past and yet the top culture of the West was Greek, not Latin.
Greek was the language of science and philosophy; Latin the
language of law, administration and business. Hadrian knew
Greek very well and had created in Rome a college of arts
which was called Athenaeum,[2] in honor of the goddess,

[1] *Decline and Fall*, chap. 3. In Bury's illustrated edition, *1*, 84.

[2] The name *Athenaeum* has become a common name in almost every
European language. Every government high school in Belgium is called
athénée. In English and other languages the word is used to designate
a literary or scientific association or club. It is one of the words which
remind us every day of our debt to antiquity, the others being *academy*,
lyceum, museum.

Athēnē, the city of Athens (which Hadrian loved) and Greek culture. Marcus Aurelius wrote his famous *Meditations* in Greek. In spite of the prestige attained by such writers as Lucretius, Cicero, Virgil and Seneca, and of the scientific books written in Latin by Vitruvius, Celsus, Frontinus and Pliny, the language of science was still predominantly Greek. It is true that the two greatest scientists of the age were born in the Orient, Ptolemy in Egypt and Galen in the province of Asia, and neither of them would have been able to write in Latin, even if they had wished to do so. But why should anyone write artificially in an inferior language, if he was able to write naturally in a superior one?

Any Roman of the second century who was intellectually ambitious had to learn Greek; the result was obtained chiefly with the help of Greek tutors or by years of "graduate study" in Athens, Alexandria or any other city in the eastern provinces. The situation can be compared to another closer to us. When Frederick the Great was king of Prussia (1740-86), he would speak German to his soldiers or servants, but French was the language of polite conversation; memoirs sent to the Berlin Academy had to be written in French or Latin, not in German, to be published.

The world in which Ptolemy lived was a Roman world, whose intellectual ideas were still predominantly Greek.

3. PTOLEMY AND HIPPARCHOS

The two outsanding men of science of the second century were Ptolemy, in the first half, and Galen in the second. They were two giants of the most genuine kind; the kind of giants who do not become smaller as the centuries pass but greater and greater. One cannot consider Ptolemy without evoking his predecessor, Hipparchos of Nicaia, who flourished in the Hellenistic Age,[3] almost three centuries before him. It is strange to think of two men separated by so large a barrier— three centuries—yet working as if the second were the immediate disciple of the first.

Hipparchos' works are lost, and it is possible that their loss was partly the result of the fact that Ptolemy's great book superseded them and made them superfluous. In some instances, Ptolemy's debt to his predecessor is acknowledged or is made clear in other ways. What we know of Hipparchos we know almost exclusively from Ptolemy, who quotes him often, sometimes verbatim.[4] Nevertheless, in the majority of cases, it is impossible to say whether the real inventor was the older or the younger man.

In what follows we shall not bother too much about that, and Ptolemy's achievements will be described as if they were exclusively or mainly his own. After all, that is the method which one cannot help following in discussing the achievements of almost any ancient scientist.

Euclid is mainly known as a mathematician, and his fame is based upon the *Elements;* Ptolemy's personality was far more complex and two of his books, the *Almagest* and the *Geography,* remained standard textbooks in their fields for at least fourteen centuries.

The comparison of Ptolemy with Euclid is a very useful one, because the fact that their books superseded earlier ones was essentially due to the same causes. Ptolemy, like Euclid,

[3] Hipparchos flourished in Rhodes from 146 to 127 and perhaps also from 161 to 146 in Alexandria.

[4] See the *index nominum* in Heiberg's edition (1907), *3* (called II), pp. 275-77.

was an excellent expositor or teacher; while their predecessors had written monographs or short treatises, they wrote very large ones of encyclopaedic nature and did it in the best order and with perfect lucidity. Both men combined an extraordinary power of synthesis and exposition with genius of the highest potential. The earlier treatises which had been the foundation of their own were soon judged to be incomplete and obsolete and the scribes ceased to copy them; thus, they were not only superseded but dropped out of existence.

4. PTOLEMY'S LIFE

It is tempting to compare Ptolemy with Euclid, two giants who shared the distinction of composing textbooks which would remain standard books in their respective fields for more than a thousand years. They are singularly alike in their greatness and in their loneliness. We know their works exceedingly well, but they themselves are practically unknown.

Ptolemy's biography is as empty as Euclid's. We do not even know when and where he was born and died. It has been said, very late (fourteenth century) that he was born in Ptolemaïs Hermeiu, a Greek city of the Thebais.[5] That is possible. He was probably a Greek Egyptian or an Egyptian Greek; he made astronomical observations in Alexandria or in Canōpos nearby from 127 to 151 (or 141?); according to an Arabic story, he lived to be seventy-eight; according to Suidas (X-2), he was still alive under Marcus Aurelius (emperor 161-80); we may conclude that he was probably born at the end of the first century.

[5] Upper Egypt, hē anō chōra. Ptolemais Hermeiu was on the site of the Egyptian village al-Minshāh.

As to his character, we have a glimpse of it in the Prooimion (or preface) to the *Almagest,* addressed to his friend Syros.[6] That preface is a noble defense of mathematics and especially of celestial mechanics. Another glimpse, indirect, is given in an early epigram:

> I know that I am mortal and ephemeral, but when I scan the crowded circling spirals of the stars I do no longer touch the earth with my feet, but side by side with Zeus I take my fill of ambrosia, the food of the gods.

This epigram is included in the Greek *Anthology* (IX, 577), bearing Ptolemy's name; this does not prove Ptolemy's authorship but is a good witness of him, like a portrait. The poet saw him as a man lifted up far above other men by his lofty purpose and equanimity.

5. THE ALMAGEST

Out of many books of his, and of his two great classics, the best known is the *Almagest.* Its curious name will be explained later when we discuss the Ptolemaic tradition. At present, let us take it for granted as most people do. The original Greek title *hē mathēmatikē syntaxis* means the *Mathematical Synthesis.* It was really a treatise of astronomy but astronomy was then a branch of mathematics; one is reminded of another classic which was published more than eighteen centuries later, Newton's *Mathematical Principles of Natural Philosophy.*

Ptolemy's astronomy, like Hipparchos', was based upon observations, his own and those of Greek and Babylonian pre-

---

[6] Syros, otherwise unknown, must have been a very good friend of Ptolemy, for the latter appeals to him thrice, "ō *Syre,*" at the beginnings of Books I and VII and at the end of Book XIII; that is the beginning, the middle and the very end of the *Almagest.*

decessors. Hipparchos had used various instruments, e.g., a celestial sphere and an improved diopter, and Ptolemy had perhaps added new instruments or improved the older ones. In this case, as in most cases, it is impossible to separate the achievements of both men and to say whether the meridian circle, the astrolabon organon, the parallactic instrument and the mural quadrant were invented by Ptolemy or improved by him or completely invented by Hipparchos. The history of instruments, we should remember, is one of the best approaches to the understanding of scientific progress, but it is full of difficulties; each instrument is developed gradually; none is created in one time for all time by a single man.[7] Their main task, however, as they undersood it, was not so much the taking and recording of observations, but the mathematical explanation of the facts which those observations revealed, and their synthesis. Therefore, the *Almagest* of Ptolemy, like the *Principia* of Newton, was primarily a mathematical book and its original title, *Mathematical Syntaxis,* was adequate.

The *Almagest* is divided into thirteen books. The first two are introductory, explaining astronomical assumptions and mathematical methods. Ptolemy proves the sphericity of the Earth and postulates the sphericity of the heavens and their revolution around the Earth immobile in the center. He discusses and redetermines the obliquity of the ecliptic. The main mathematical method is trigonometry, for Ptolemy realized that spherical geometry and graphical means were inconvenient and insufficient. In this he was not independent of

---

[7] For general considerations on instruments, see Maurice Daumas, *Les instruments scientifiques aux XVIIᵉ et XVIIIᵉ siècles* (Paris, 1953: *Isis 44,* 391). Daumas deals with late instruments, but many of his remarks apply just as well to the ancient ones.

Hipparchos but, in addition, he was privileged to stand upon the shoulders of Menelaos of Alexandria.

The trigonometry is explained in chapters numbered 11 and 13 in Heiberg's edition. Every distance on the sphere is an angular one; the measurement of angles is replaced by the consideration of the chords subtending the corresponding arcs.[8] The circle is divided into 360° and the diameter into 120 parts. Ptolemy used sexagesimal numbers in order to avoid the embarrassment of fractions (that is the way he put it, *Almagest* I, 10). Thus, each of the 60 parts of the radius was divided into sixty small parts, and these again were divided into sixty smaller ones.[9] A table of chords was computed for every half degree, from 0° to 180°,[10] each chord being expressed in parts of the radius, minutes and seconds. The size of some chords (sides of regular polygons) could be derived easily from Euclid; the size of others was obtained, thanks

---

[8] Later on, Arabic astronomers inspired by Hindu ones replaced the chords by sines and other ratios, but the purpose of Ptolemaic (Hipparchian) trigonometry was the same as ours. Assuming the radius to be the unit,

$$\text{chord } a = 2 \sin \ (a/2)$$
$$\sin \ a = (\tfrac{1}{2}) \text{ chord } (2a) .$$

[9] In Latin, the small parts were called *partes* minutae *primae,* and the smaller ones, *partes minutae* secundae. Our words *minutes* and *seconds* were stupidly derived from the first adjective in the first expression and from the second in the second.

[10] Ptolemy's table of chords, as given in the *Almagest* (I, 11), is thus like a table of sines for every quarter degree from 1° to 90°. The sines which could be obtained from his table would be correct to 5 places. The table allowed him to determine *pi* with remarkable precision. Let us assume that the length of the circumference is very close to 360 times the chord of 1°, each of which measures 1 part 2′50″. *Pi* is the ratio of the circumference to the diameter, or 360/120 (1 part 2′50″) = 3 parts 8′30″ = 3.14166 (real value 3.14159...).

to Ptolemy's theorem about quadrilaterals inscribed in a circle; that theorem enabled one to find the chord of a sum of angles. Opposite the value of each chord in the table is given 1/30 of the excess of that chord over the preceding one; this 1/30 is expressed in minutes, seconds and thirds; this would enable one to compute the chords for every minute of angle. Ptolemy understood the meaning of interpolations and approximations; his correct appreciation of them was one of the bases of applied mathematics.

The table of chords is followed by a geometrical argument leading to the calculation of the relations of arcs of the equator, ecliptic, horizon and meridian, and tables *ad hoc*. The same kind of discussion is continued in Book II with reference to the length of the longest day at a given latitude.

Book III deals with the length of the year and the motion of the Sun, Ptolemy using epicycles and eccentrics (the first of which certainly and the second probably invented by Apollōnios of Perga, III-2 B.C.).

Book IV. Length of the month and theory of the Moon. This contained what is supposed to be one of his discoveries (as distinguished from those of Hipparchos), the second inequality of the Moon called evection. He fixed the amount of it at 1°19′30″, and accounted for it in terms of eccentrics and epicycles and of a small oscillation (prosneusis) of the epicycle. This is a good example of mathematical ingenuity.[11]

Book V. Construction of the astrolabe. Theory of the Moon

[11] The evection, caused by the Sun's attraction, depends upon the alternate increase and decrease of the eccentricity of the Moon's orbit; the eccentricity is maximum when the Sun is crossing the line of the apses (syzygies) and minimum at the quadratures. The value of the evection is about 1° 15′, and its period, about 1⅛ year.

continued. Diameters of the Sun, Moon, Earth's shadow, distance of the Sun, dimensions of the Sun, Moon and Earth.

Book VI. Solar and lunar eclipses.

Book VII-VIII. Stars. Precession of the equinoxes. The table of stars covers the end of VII and the beginning of VIII. The rest of VIII describes the Milky Way and the construction of a celestial globe.

Books IX-XIII. Planetary motions. This is perhaps the most original part of the *Almagest,* because Hipparchos had not been able to complete his own synthesis of planetary systems. Book IX deals with generalities, such as the order of the planets according to their distances from the Earth and periods of revolution; then with Mercury. Book X—Venus; XI—Jupiter and Saturn; XII—Stationary points and retrogressions, greatest elongations of Mercury and Venus; XIII—Motions of planets in latitude, inclinations and magnitudes of their orbits.

In short, the *Almagest* was a survey of the astronomical knowledge available about 150 A.D., and that knowledge was not essentially different from that attained in 150 B.C. It is impossible to discuss the details of it without discussing the whole of ancient astronomy. Let us consider a few points.

First the *Almagest* defined what we call the "Ptolemaic system," that is, the solar system centered upon the Earth. Following Hipparchos, Ptolemy rejected the ideas of Aristarchos of Samos (III-1 B.C.), who had anticipated the Copernican system; Hipparchos and Ptolemy rejected those ideas[12] because they did not tally sufficiently well with the observations. Their objections were of the same nature as Tycho

---

[12] They even rejected the geoheliocentric system of Hēracleidēs of Pontos (IV-2 B.C.). The Ptolemaic system was completely geocentrical.

Brahe's at the end of the sixteenth century; a sufficient agreement between observations and the Aristarchian or Copernican ideas became possible only when Kepler replaced circular trajectories by elliptic ones (1609). The methodic excellence of the *Almagest* caused the supremacy of the Ptolemaic system until the sixteenth century, in spite of abundant criticisms which became more and more acute as observations increased in number and precision.

One might say that Hipparchos and Ptolemy were backward in two respects, because they rejected the heliocentrical ideas of Aristarchos and the ellipses of Apollōnios, but such a conclusion would be very unfair. Men of science are not prophets; they see a little further than other men but can never completely shake off the prejudices of their own environment. As heliocentricity did not lead to greater simplicity or precision, their rejection of it was justified.

The *Catalogue of Stars* is the earliest catalogue which has come down to us. It includes 1,028 stars and gives the longitude, latitude and magnitude of each. It was largely derived from Hipparchos'[13] catalogue of c. 130 B.C.; Ptolemy left the latitudes unchanged but added 2°40′ to every longitude in order to take the precession into account. The precession of the equinoxes had been discovered by Hipparchos on the basis of earlier observations, Babylonian and Greek. The precession amounts to little more than one degree per century;[14] con-

[13] Hipparchos had listed not many more than 850 stars giving the latitude, longitude and magnitude of each.

[14] Hipparchos assumed that the precession amounted to 45″ or 46″ a year, which would add up to 1.°3 in a century; Ptolemy corrected that to 36″, which is exactly 1° a century. The real value is 50.″25, equivalent to 1.°4 a century. Hipparchos was closer to the truth than Ptolemy.

sidering the observational means of the ancient astronomers, it is clear that they could not discover it without the knowledge of stellar longitudes antedating their own by many centuries.

Before abandoning Ptolemaic astronomy, a few words must be said of the methods of projection, orthographic and stereographic, in spite of the fact that they are not explained in the *Almagest* but in separate monographs.[15] It is possible that both methods were invented by Hipparchos; at any rate, Ptolemy's explanation of them is the earliest available.

Both methods were needed to solve a fundamental problem, the representation of points or arcs of the spherical surface of heaven[16] upon a plane (or map). In the *Analēmma* method, the points and arcs were projected orthogonally upon three planes mutually at right angles, the meridian, horizon and prime vertical; this method was used chiefly to find the position of the Sun at a given hour. The method of the *Planisphaerium* was what is now called stereographic projection. Every point of the sphere is represented by its projection upon the equator from the opposite pole (the northern hemisphere was projected by Ptolemy from the south pole). This particular system of projection had very remarkable and useful properties, of which Ptolemy was aware though he did

[15] The orthogonal projection is explained in the *Analēmma* (meaning taking-up, Aufnahme, also sundial), and the stereographic in the *Planisphaerium*, both lost in Greek but preserved in Latin translations from the Arabic. Latest editions, by J. L. Heiberg, in the *Ptolemaei Opera* (2, 187-223, 225-59, 1907). The second was translated into German by J. Drecker (*Isis 9*, 255-78, 1927), who summarized the tradition of the *Planisphaerium* in his preface.

[16] All the stars and planets were supposed, for geometrical purposes, to move on a single sphere. That was all right; if a star was not on the sphere, its central projection on it was considered; the angular distances remained the same.

not give general proofs of them. The projection of all circles are circles (with the apparent exception of circles passing through the pole which are projected as straight lines). The stereographic projection is the only one which is both conformal and perspective,[17] Ptolemy could not have known that unicity, but he had made a good study of projections and was lucky.

6. THE GEOGRAPHY

Ptolemy's geographical treatise or guide (*geōgraphicē hyphēgēsis*) is almost as important as the *Almagest*. It covered the whole of mathematical geography, just as the *Almagest* covered the whole of mathematical astronomy, and it influenced geography as deeply and as long as the *Almagest* influenced astronomy. During fourteen centuries, at least, the *Almagest* was the standard book, or call it the Bible, of astronomy, while the *Geography* was the Bible of geography. The name Ptolemy meant geography to geographers and astronomy to astronomers.

The *Geography* was composed after the *Almagest,* say, after 150. It was divided into eight books and was restricted to mathematical geography and to all the information needed for the drawing of accurate maps. His knowledge was derived mainly from Eratosthenēs, Hipparchos, Strabōn (I-2 B.C.), and, above all, from Marinos of Tyre (II-1), whom he praised yet criticized.

---

[17] A conformal projection is one in which the angles between two intersected curves are the same in projection. A perspective projection is one in which there is a 1 to 1 correspondence between any point on the sphere and its projection on the plane.

The first to prove that the stereographical projections of spherical circles are circles was Jordanus Nemorarius (XIII-1).

We know Marinos only through Ptolemy, who paid a very moving tribute to him in chapter 5 of Book I and referred to him many times; we may be sure that he quoted Marinos fairly, even when he disagreed with him. The relationship of Ptolemy to Marinos is very much like his relationship to Hipparchos, the great difference being that Marinos flourished not long before Ptolemy,[18] while Hipparchos was three centuries distant.

Ptolemy put together the geographical contributions of his predecessors and his own and thus created the first general treatise on geography. He was not interested in physical and human geography as Strabōn and Pliny were, and it is not fair to reproach him for not having dealt with subjects which did not concern him.

Book I discusses generalities, the size of the Earth and of the known world, methods of cartographic projection, etc. Books II to VII are systematic descriptions of the world in the form of tables giving the longitudes and latitudes of places, for every country of which he had sufficient knowledge. Ptolemy (or Marinos) was the first to speak of longitudes and latitudes (mēcos, platos) as we do, meaning the distance in longitude or latitude to a zero circle. Some 8,000 places, "remarkable cities" (poleis episēmoi), rivers, etc., are listed. The identification of many of those places is very difficult, if not impossible, in spite of abundant investigations by scholars very familiar with the regions concerned. The world which he tried to describe extended roughly from 20 S to 65 N and

---

[18] Ptolemy called him (Geography 1, 6) "the latest of our age" (hystatos te tōn cath' hēmas) which is not quite clear; he does not say that he knew him personally. Hence, Marinos was a late predecessor, how late? Hipparchos was also, in some respects, a late predecessor.

from the Canary Islands at the extreme west to some 180° eastward from them. The tables made it possible to draw maps wherein every item would be placed at its proper latitude and longitude; such maps were probably included in the proto-type manuscripts, because there are definite references to them in Book VIII, which is a kind of astronomical epilogue. The earliest manuscripts that have come to us are considerably later, say, thirteenth century, but may represent a tradition going back to Ptolemy and Marinos.

Ptolemy's intentions were excellent, but their realization very imperfect. He was right in believing that in order to pro-duce an accurate map, one must first prepare a net of meridians and parallels, and his method of projection was distinctly superior to Marinos'. When the net is ready, one may easily mark upon it as many places as possible, the coordinates of which are known. So far so good, but the map will be true only if those coordinates have been established by astrono-mical methods. Unfortunately, very few latitudes were cor-rectly determined and no longitudes at all (the means were lacking). His coordinates were computed on the basis of dead reckonings, itineraries, traveller's tales and very few scientific observations. His theory of projection was very much better than the data to be projected! The net itself was insufficient, because his estimate of the Earth's size was inaccurate and be-cause his first meridian was wobbly.

The central degree of latitude was our 36° (Gibraltar, Rhodos) and that was convenient. The prime meridian was drawn through the Fortunate Islands (Canaries plus Madeiras); thus all the longitudes would extend only on the east side of 0°. Unfortunately, the relationship of that first meridian to the continent was very inaccurate. As to the size of the Earth, Ptolemy had preferred the estimate of Poseidōnios (I-1 B.C.) to that far more correct one of Eratosthenēs (III-2 B.C.).[19] His estimate of the length of the Eurasian continent was much exaggerated, 180° instead of 130°. This would eventually increase the hopes of Columbus and early circumnavigators but was poor geography.

There is not much point in criticizing his views of the unknown part of the world, for such views could only be worthless guesses. For example, his rejection of the circumambient ocean[20] was not more arbitrary than its acceptance by earlier geographers.

The tradition of every Greek text is open to doubts because the earliest manuscripts that have come down to us are always many centuries late. In the case of the *Geography*, the difficulties are much increased by the necessity of considering two traditions which may have concurred or not, the literary tradition and the cartographic one. I am willing to accept the conclusions of one of the greatest scholars, Father Joseph Fischer, S. J.,[21] who devoted the best part of his life to that subject—that the maps which have come down to us in the earliest manuscripts (none earlier than the thirteenth century,

[19] According to Eratosthenēs, the circumference of the Earth was 252,-000 stadia; according to Poseidōnios, 180,000 stadia. This might be the same measurement, if the stadia used in both cases were in the ratio 20/21. If Eratosthenēs' stadia were 10 to a mile, then his measurement equalled 37,495 km. (close to the real value 40,120 km.). For details, see Aubrey Diller, "Ancient Measurements of the Earth" (*Isis 40* [1949], 6-9).

[20] The Homeric views of the circumambient ocean were probably of Phoenician origin. However far the Phoenicians might sail, they were always stopped by the ocean. Hērodotos was alone in his scepticism about it (*History of Science*, pp. 138, 186, 310, 510, 526).

[21] Joseph Fischer, S. J. (1858-1944). See *Isis (37, 183)*.

eleven centuries later than the lost prototypes) go back, even as the text; to Ptolemy or even to Marinos (it is hardly possible to distinguish between these two). The production of a world map was Ptolemy's definite aim;[22] he may have failed to produce it himself, and later maps, by Agathodaimōn of Alexandria or others, may have been graphical representations of the tables. Certain knowledge is out of the question, but I prefer to share Father Fischer's confidence than Bagrow's hypercriticism.[23]

On the Ptolemaic maps, meridians are drawn for every 5° and marked so in the margin, but parallels are established according to the length of the longest day (for every quarter-hour difference). In the *Geography* (I, 23), there is a table giving lengths of day with corresponding latitudes.[24] This part of the tradition goes back to the Eratosthenian concept of climata: zones of the Earth's surface at such a distance from each other that the average length of the longest day differs by half an hour from the one to the other. There were seven such climata, because there was no room for more in the known world, ranging from a longest day of thirteen hours in

[22] *Geography* (1, 2, 2). Text quoted in Greek and Latin in *Isis* (*20*, 269).
[23] Leo Bagrow, *The Origin of Ptolemy's Geographia* (Stockholm, 1946; *Isis 37*, 187). According to Bagrow, the text of the *Geography* is a late Byzantine compilation (say, tenth or eleventh century) and the maps, as we have them, are later than the text, say, thirteenth century. Such claims can be neither proved nor disproved.
[24] There is a similar table in the *Almagest* (XII, 6) wherein the latitudes are expressed with more precision in degrees and minutes. In the *Geography*, they are expressed in degrees and *Egyptian* fractions. Thus, to 13 hours correspond in the *Almagest* lat. 16°27′, in the *Geography* 16 1/3 1/12° ($= 16°25′$). Aubrey Diller, "The Parallels on Ptolemaic Maps" (*Isis 33*, 5-7, 1941).

Meroë (in Nubia, lat. 17° N) to one of sixteen hours at the Borysthenēs (Dnieper).

Ptolemy was aware of the imperfection of his knowledge and of the indetermination of his data, but the tabular form obliging him to state for each place definite latitudes and longitudes gave an impression of far greater exactness than was warranted, and his followers' assumption of the correctness of those numbers was the cause of many errors.

The knowledge of the world revealed in the *Geography* is often inaccurate, but its extent and diversity are, nevertheless, astonishing. Consider, for example, the data relative to equatorial Africa, the Upper Nile and the equatorial mountains (Lunae Mons, *Geography* IV, 8). This is the more remarkable, if one bears in mind the confusion of ideas which still obtained as late as the third quarter of the last century.[25]

7. PTOLEMY'S OPTICS

In speaking of Euclid's *Optics* I remarked that he dealt with a few phenomena in a geometrical way. Two optical treatises are ascribed to Ptolemy; one, entitled in Latin *Ptolomei de speculis,* has been restituted to Hērōn of Alexandria, who flourished possibly before Ptolemy; the other, called Ptolemy's *Optics,* has come down to us in a Latin version made from the Arabic in 1154 by Eugene of Palermo (XII-2).[26]

This second treatise, the only one which we need consider here, is divided into five books, but Book I and the end of

[25] *Intro.* (*3*, 1158-60).
[26] Hērōn, wrongly placed in my *Introduction* (*1*, 208), flourished after 62 and before 150 (*Isis 30*, 140; *32*, 263-66). Latin-German edition of *De speculis* by Wilhelm Schmidt (*Heronis opera, 2*, 301-65, 1900). Gilberto Govi, *L'ottica di Tolomeo de Eugenio* (Torino, 1885). Lejeune is preparing a new edition of this text.

Book V are lost. Such as it has come to us, it is very different from Euclid's work, being physical and even psychological, for Ptolemy tried to explain vision in concrete sensual terms. His effort was understandable but premature, for the anatomical and physiological knowledge of the eye was still utterly insufficient.[27]

Books III and IV deal with catoptrics and constitute the most elaborate study of mirrors which has come down to us from antiquity. Book V deals with refraction and includes a table of refraction from air to water which is remarkable enough to be reproduced here.[28]

i	r	first difference	real value of r	error
10°	8°		7°28′	+32′
		7°30′		
20°	15°30′		14°51′	+39′
		7°		
30°	22°30′		22°1′	+29′
		6°30′		
40°	29°		28°49′	+11′
		6°		
50°	35°		35°3′	−3′
		5°30′		
60°	40°30′		40°30′	0
		5°		
70°	45°30′		44°48′	+42′
		4°30′		
80°	50°		47°36′	+2°24′

[27] Albert Lejeune, "Les tables de réfraction de Ptolémée" (*Annales de la Société scientifique de Bruxelles 60* [1946], 93-101); "Les lois de la réflection dans l'Optique de Ptolémée" (*L'antiquité classique 15* [1947], 241-56; *Isis 39*, 244); *Euclide et Ptolémée. Deux stades de l'optique géométrique grecque* (Louvain, 1948), *Isis 40*, 278).

[28] Figures as given by Lejeune, 1946 (p. 94).

That table is unique in classical literature, and it astonished historians of physics so much that they took it too readily at its face value. Ptolemy's study of refraction was spoken of as the most remarkable experimental research of antiquity. I am sorry to have to confess that I helped to diffuse that judgment,[29] which has proved since to be erroneous; or, to put it otherwise, Ptolemy's results are still very remarkable but in an unexpected way.

Looking at the first differences in column 3, one immediately sees that they form an arithmetical series, the difference between two successive terms being $\frac{1}{2}°$. Now, can that be the result of observations? (Note the observational errors in the last column.) It is certain that Ptolemy made some observations with care; he did not continue them, however, but generalized them prematurely, and built his table a priori. Lejeune has suggested that he may have been misled by early Greek authorities or by Babylonian examples. Constancy of second differences may be noticed in polygonal numbers and some tables of the Sun show that Chaldean astronomers had tried to account for the Sun's irregular speed by constant second differences.

The ancients did not yet understand the supremacy of observations as we do and used observational results rather as indicators justifying the formulation of a theory, even as guideposts help travellers to find the right path. Before judging them too severely, we should remember that their observational means were generally so poor that the results of observations could not possibly have with them the same authority as they have with us.

[29] *Intro.* (*1*, 274).

As Ptolemy was unfamiliar with sines, one could not expect him to discover the law of refraction,[30] but it is interesting to examine his results from that hindsight point of view. Let us call the angles of incidence and refraction enumerated in his table a and b. The average ratio sin a/sin b is 1.311, with an average error of 0.043; the ratio a/b, however, is 1.42 with an average error of 0.044.[31] Hence, Ptolemy's results, as given in his table, would not have enabled him to find the constancy of sin a/sin b; that is, he would have risked, instead, finding the constancy of a/b; he would have found a wrong law instead of the true one.

At any rate, Ptolemy understood very clearly the fact that a ray of light is deviated when it passes from one medium into another of different density (as we would put it), and he explained the error caused by refraction in astronomical observations. It is disturbing, however, to find no mention of atmospheric refraction in the *Almagest;* we must conclude that the *Optics* was written by Ptolemy after the *Almagest,*[32] or that it was written by somebody else. The subject was not tackled again until much later, by Ibn al-Haitham (XI-1); for the first accurate determinations one had to wait until Tycho Brahe

---

[30] The law was discovered by Willebrord Snel in 1618; published again by Descartes in 1637.

[31] The figures quoted are taken from Ernst Gerland, *Geschichte der Physik* (p. 124, München, 1913; *Isis 1,* 527-29).

[32] I prefer the first hypothesis. Having discovered refraction, Ptolemy could conceive the idea of atmospheric refraction. This is maximum at the horizon (almost 35′) and creates phenomena (e.g., at sunset or sunrise) which must or may puzzle the intelligent observer. A knowledge of refraction (cataclasis), even atmospheric refraction, is ascribed also to Cleomēdēs, who may be posterior to Ptolemy, in spite of my having classified him tentatively under (I-1 B.C.).

(1580), Kepler (1604), and the first Cassini, Jean Dominique (c. 1661).

8. THE TETRABIBLOS

Among the various other works ascribed to Ptolemy, I must select for discussion his astrological treatise, in spite of the fact that many men of science would refuse to consider it.[33] Two astrological books bear his name, the *Tetrabiblos* (*Quadripartitum*) and the *Carpos* (*Fructus*);[34] according to the consensus of scholarly opinion, the first is genuine, the second apocryphal. These two books have been transmitted together in Greek and other languages, in manuscript and printed traditions, but for our purpose, it will suffice to consider the first.

Many scholars have claimed that the same man could not possibly be the author of the rational *Almagest* and of the *Tetrabiblos*, which is chockful of irrational assumptions. They forget that astrology was the scientific religion of Ptolemy's day. At a time when the old mythology had become untenable, the sidereal religion had gradually taken its place in the minds of men who were loyal to pagan traditions as well as scientifically minded. Stemming from Greek astronomy and Chaldean astrology, it was a compromise between the popular religion and monotheism; the concept of sidereal immortality which it fostered reconciled astronomy with religion; it was a kind

[33] I have claimed repeatedly that if we would understand ancient science and culture we must take the errors and superstitions into account as well as the progressive achievements. See, e.g., my *History of Science* (1952), p. xiii.

[34] *Fructus* is the translation of *Carpos*, but the Latin title more commonly used is *Centiloquium*, referring to the fact that that booklet is a collection of a hundred aphorisms. The author was probably a court astrologer who flourished after Ptolemy and before Proclos (V-2).

of scientific pantheism indorsed by men of science as well as by philosophers, especially by neo-Platonists and Stoics.

We now realize that such a compromise, however useful it may have been in a period of confusion and distress, was very dangerous; there was a fatal ambiguity in the astrological creed, in that it claimed to be science and religion at the same time. It was a poor application of good science, and the religious side of it had the weakness of any superstition. There has never been a better example of pseudo-science and pseudo-religion. Yet, it prospered for a few centuries in the religious vacuum caused by the repudiation of the old mythology. It would be very unfair to blame Ptolemy for having failed to understand eighteen hundred years ago what many of our own contemporaries have not yet understood today. The ambiguities obtaining between rational knowledge and creed are still cultivated by pragmatists, by Christian scientists, and other sectarians who handle religion and science in the way thimble-riggers cause balls or peas to vanish or reappear.

The *Tetrabiblos* is dedicated to the same Syros whom Ptolemy called upon thrice in the *Almagest*. What is more convincing, its style is similar to that of the *Almagest*. It is a great pity, however, that Ptolemy wrote it, because the prestige of his name was fully exploited, and the fame of the *Tetrabiblos* was not only equal to that of the *Almagest,* but much greater.

In his excellent book on *Hellenistic Civilization*,[35] Professor Tarn has developed the view that the triumph of astrology was assured when Hipparchos and Ptolemy rejected

[35] First published in 1927; I quote from the third edition revised by W. W. Tarn and G. T. Griffith (pp. 298, 348, London, Arnold, 1952).

the heliocentric system of Aristarchos. That theory does not hold water. In the first place, the postulates of astrology are independent of whether the Sun or the Earth is the center of our planetary system; in the second place, astrology did not stop after the acceptance of the Copernican system but continued to grow lustily. Kepler himself drew horoscopes. Our country is leading the world in astronomy, and we have every right to be proud of that, but if we be honest, we cannot accept praise for our astronomers without accepting full blame for our astrologers. There are more astrologers than astronomers in America and some of them, at least, earn considerably more than the latter; the astrological publications are far more popular than the astronomical; almost every newspaper has an astrological column which has to be paid for and would not be published at all if a large number of people did not want it.

Astrology was perhaps excusable in the social and spiritual disarray of Hellenistic and Roman days; it is unforgivable today. The professional astrologers of our time are fools or crooks or both, and they ought to be restrained, but who will do it? Astronomers are too busy with their own work and find it unnecessary to castigate obvious errors; they do not want to get into trouble, for in a trial ignorant judges or jurymen might decide that astrologers have as much right to express their views as the astronomers. And yet to ignore a contagious disease is the worst way of dealing with it. If one wishes to cure it, one must first throw light upon it and show it for what it is.

Superstitions are like diseases, highly contagious diseases. We should be indulgent to Ptolemy, who had innocently accepted the prejudices endemic in his age and could not foresee their evil consequences, but the modern diffusion of astrological superstitions deserves no mercy, and the newspaper

61

owners who do not hesitate to spread lies for the sake of money should be punished just as one punishes the purveyors of adulterated food.

To return to the *Tetrabiblos*,[36] Ptolemy refers to the *Almagest* in his general introduction and explains that the *Almagest* is a mathematical book dealing with matters which can be demonstrated, while the new book deals with matters which are less tangible and highly conjectural, yet deserve to be investigated. One has the impression that in his old age, when Ptolemy had completed his scientific work, he applied himself to meta-astronomy and tried to justify as well as he could the astrological prejudices of his time, prejudices which he fully shared. The first chapters constitute an apology for divination and particularly for astrology. Granted the almost universal belief in divination, divination by the stars and planets seemed less irrational, "more scientific," than divination by means of birds, entrails, dreams or other *omina*. Ptolemy added that the possibility and occurrence of error should not discourage the astrologer any more than they discourage the pilot or the physician (I, 2).

The *Tetrabiblos* is a compilation of Chaldean, Egyptian and Greek folklore and of earlier writings, especially those of Poseidōnios,[37] which is so complete and so well-ordered that it

[36] The original title seems to have been *Mathēmatikē tetrabiblos syntaxis,* which was strangely enough the same title as that of the *Almagest,* plus the neutral word *tetrabiblos.* That title was erroneous and misleading, for the *Tetrabiblos* is definitely not a mathematical treatise. Some MSS are entitled *Ta pros Syron apotelesmatika (Prognostics dedicated to Syros).* Prognostics was a correct title and meaningful. The most common title, however, is *Tetrabiblos,* which means "four books," and is as cryptic as *Centiloquium.*

[37] Poseidōnios is not named in the *Tetrabiblos,* but Franz Boll has shown, in his *Studien über Claudius Ptolemäus* (Leipzig, 1894) that the

remained a standard work until our own days. In that it was even more successful than the *Almagest,* for the simple reason that astronomy being a science was bound to develop and change, while modern astrology is essentially the same as the ancient one. Superstitions may change but do not progress; in fact, they do not change much, because they are exceedingly conservative. The *Almagest* is published anew from time to time for scholarly purposes, but has no practical value; on the other hand, new editions of the *Tetrabiblos* are issued for the guidance of practising astrologers.[38]

The contents of the four books of the *Tetrabiblos* may be roughly described as follows: I. Generalities concerning astrology and the planets. Beneficent and maleficent planets, masculine and feminine ones, diurnal and nocturnal, etc. II. Catholic astrology, astrological geography and ethnography. Prognostications of a general kind, applying to races, countries, cities or to catastrophies which affect many men at the same time, such as wars, famines, plagues, earthquakes, floods, or the weather, seasons and climes (latitudes). III. Genethlialogical prognostications relative to individuals. IV. Fortune. Astrological aspects of material fortune, personal dignity (axiōma), degree of activity, marriage, children, friends and enemies, foreign travel, quality of death, various periods of life. In Robbins' Greek-English edition (Loeb Library), the four

author of *Tetrabiblos* used the lost writings of Poseidōnios, especially for what concerns the defense of astrology and astrological ethnography (Book II). In many geographical details, *Tetrabiblos* and the *Geography* do not agree, but it does not follow that the authors of those two works are different.

[38] An English edition published for the astrological market in Chicago, 1936, was reviewed in *Isis* (*35,* 181).

books cover, respectively, 116, 104, 152 and 87 pages; and the whole Greek text extends to 230 pages.

One cannot read the whole of that treatise or a part of it without being terribly dismayed. If Ptolemy was really the author of it, it is a thousand pities, but that only shows that he was a man of his clime and time. Even the greatest genius cannot transcend all those limitations at once.

9. THE PTOLEMAIC TRADITION

We shall outline only the tradition of his three most famous works, the *Almagest,* the *Cosmography,* and the *Tetrabiblos.*

TRADITION OF THE ALMAGEST

The Greek tradition was solidly established from the beginning and it was kept alive by the commentaries of a series of illustrious mathematicians, Pappos (III-2), Theōn of Alexandria (IV-2), Hypatia (V-1) and Proclos (V-2). The book entitled *Mathēmatikē syntaxis* was often called *Megalē syntaxis* (the great collection) or even *Megistē syntaxis* (the very great collection).

The importance of the Arabic tradition is symbolized by the common name *Almagest* which combines the Arabic article with the Greek adjective *megistē.* Arabic mathematicians were acquainted with the book very early, for it was translated into Arabic by an unknown scholar at the insistence of the illustrious wazīr, Yaḥyā ibn Khālid ibn Barmak (Joannes the Barmecide), who lived from 738 to 805; it was translated again in 829, on the basis of a Syriac version, by al-Ḥajjāj ibn Yūsuf (IX-1) and a third time by Isḥāq ibn Ḥunain (IX-2), and Isḥāq's translation was corrected by Thābit ibn Qurra (IX-2). Further editions and adaptations were prepared by such eminent men as Abū-l-Wafā' (X-2) and Naṣīr al-dīn al-Ṭūsī (XIII-2).

Meanwhile, the Arabic geographers had produced astronomical treatises which were not translations of the *Almagest*, yet were profoundly indebted to it. The first of these treatises was the one by al-Farghānī (IX-1) which became in the original Arabic and in Latin and Hebrew versions one of the main sources of Ptolemaic astronomy until the Renaissance. The same can be said of al-Battānī's treatise (IX-2), but though it was far superior to al-Farghānī's, it was less popular. Moreover, since al-Battānī was a greater mathematician and a more original mind than al-Farghānī, he modified the Ptolemaic tradition more deeply.

Not only was it possible to read the *Almagest* in Arabic, and the treatises of al-Farghānī and al-Battānī which were derived from it, but the Muslim astronomers worked so well that they were soon able to criticize Ptolemy's ideas. As the astronomical observations were more numerous and more precise, it became increasingly difficult to reconcile them with the theories. The philosopher, Ibn Bājja (Avempace, XII-1), expressed the difficulties and this was soon done with more authority by Jābir ibn Aflaḥ (XII-1) in his treatise called *Iṣlāḥ al-magisṭi,* (the Correction of the *Almagest*). Other Muslims, the philosopher Ibn Ṭufail (XII-2) and his disciple al-Biṭrūjī (XII-2) thought of solving the difficulties by rejecting Ptolemy's eccentrics and epicycles and reverting to the earlier theory of homocentric spheres which had been endorsed by Aristotle himself. After the twelfth century, the vicissitudes of astronomical theory were largely the result of a protracted struggle between the followers of Ptolemy and those of Aristotle.[39]

[39] For more details, see *Intro. 2*, 16-19; *3*, 110-37, 1105-21.

Within the twelfth century, the *Almagest* as well as the treatises of Alfraganus and Albategnius[40] became all of them available in Latin. Alfraganus was first translated by John of Seville (XII-1) in 1134, then again by Plato of Tivoli (XII-1).

The *Almagest* was translated from Greek into Latin, in Sicily, c. 1160, and from Arabic into Latin by Gerard of Cremona (XII-2) in Toledo in 1175. Such was the prestige of the Arabic source or of the Toledo academy that the indirect translation of 1175 displaced the direct one of 1160.

Gerald did not simply translate the *Almagest,* but he translated the Iṣlah al-majisṭī as well, before 1187[41] (that is, when Jābir's work was still a novelty in Muslim circles).

The Hebrew translations were a little slower in appearing; they belong to the thirteenth century. The summary of the *Almagest* written by Ibn Rushd (Averroes, XII-2), the Arabic text of which is lost, was translated into Hebrew by Jacob Anaṭoli (XIII-1), and the same translated also, c. 1232, al-Farghānī's treatise from Latin and Arabic into Hebrew. Moses ibn Tibbon (XIII-2) translated into Hebrew al-Biṭrūjī in 1259 and Jābir ibn Aflaḥ in 1274.

Finally, we may mention, for the sake of curiosty, the Syriac summary of the *Almagest* written by Abū-l-Faraj in 1279; this was probably the redaction of his lectures on the subject delivered at Marāgha between 1272 and 1279.

In short, during the medieval period, every astronomer, whether Jewish, Christian or Muslim, might be assumed to be familiar with Ptolemaic astronomy, directly or indirectly; we might even say that every one was a Ptolemaist with few, if

[40] Meaning al-Farghānī (IX-1) and al-Battānī (IX-2).
[41] 1187 is the year of Gerard's death in Toledo. Jābir (Latin, Geber) died about the middle of the twelfth century.

any, qualifications. The history of medieval astronomy is a history of Ptolemaic ideas and of a growing discontent with them. The difficulties could not be solved with cinematical expedients, nor could they be solved by replacing the Sun in the center instead of the Earth. The main stumbling block was the notion that celestial trajectories must be circular (or combinations of circles) and that block was removed only by Kepler as late as 1609.

The history of the Ptolemaic tradition includes the history of astronomical tables, all of which were ultimately derived from those of the *Almagest*.

One more aspect of the Ptolemaic tradition must be indicated, however. The *Almagest* consecrated the use of sexagesimal fractions, and obstructed the natural extension of decimal numbers to decimal fractions; or to put it otherwise, it discouraged the use of decimal submultiples in the same manner that decimal multiples were used. The superiority of decimal fractions was well explained for the first time by the Fleming Simon Stevin in 1585, and their exclusive use has not been obtained to this day.

With the slowness of progress, or the persistance of Ptolemaic errors, the geocentric error was not proved until 1543 by Copernicus, the sexagesimal error not until 1585 by Stevin, the circular error not until 1609 by Kepler.

The first printed edition of Ptolemaic astronomy was al-Farghānī's treatise as Latinized by John of Seville (XII-1), *Compilatio astronomica* (Ferrara, 1493. Klebs no. 51. Facsimiles of both sides of first leaf, *Osiris 5*, 141).

The *Epitoma in Almagestum* by Regiomontanus (XV-2) was printed three years later (Venice, 1496. Klebs no. 841.1. Facsimile of title page, *Osiris 5*, 162).

So much for the incunabula.

The first printed editions of the *Almagest* are the following: Latin version from the Arabic by Gerard of Cremona, Toledo, 1175, edited by Peter Liechtenstein (Venice, 1515).

Latin version from the Greek by George of Trebizond, 1451, edited by Luca Gaurico (Venice, Junta, 1528) .

First Greek text, edited by Simon Grynaeus, made upon the Bēssariōn manuscript once used by Regiomontanus (Basel, Walderus, 1538). Facsimile of title page (*Isis 36,* 256).

The following indications may be of interest.

First printed edition of al-Battānī (IX-2), in the Latin translation by Plato of Tivoli (XII-1) (Nürnberg, Joh. Petreius, 1537). Splendid Arabic-Latin edition by C. A. Nallino (3 vols., Milano, 1899-1907) .

First printed editions of the *Iṣlāḥ al-majisṭī* of Jābir ibn Aflaḥ (XII-1) as Latinized by Gerard of Cremona before 1187 (Nürnberg, Joh. Petreius, 1534).

First printed edition of al-Biṭrūjī (XII-2), as Latinized by Qalonymous ben David in 1528-29 (Venice, Junta, 1531). The tradition of this text is curious. It was translated from Arabic into Latin by Michael Scot in 1217,[42] from Arabic into Hebrew by Moses ibn Tibbon in 1259, from Hebrew into Latin by Qalonymos.

To these printed texts a good many others could be added, even if one restrict oneself to the pre-Copernican period (pre-1543). It will suffice to mention the many editions of the *Sphaera mundi* by Joannes de Sacrobosco (XIII-1) , which was slavishly derived from al-Farghānī and al-Battānī. There are thirty-one separate incunabular editions of the *Sphaera,* plus many others in combination with other texts.[43]

---

[42] Michael Scot's translation was recently edited by Francis J. Carmody (Berkeley, Calif., 1952; *Isis 44,* 280-81) .

[43] For Sacrobosco, see Klebs (nos. 874, 875). Lynn Thorndike, *The Sphere and its Commentators* (Chicago, 1949; *Isis 40,* 257-63).

TRADITIONS OF THE GEOGRAPHY (OR COSMOGRAPHY)

The early tradition of the *Cosmography* is not by any means as well known as that of the *Almagest*. We have already explained that in this case it does not suffice to consider the text, but there is also a cartographic tradition which is very mysterious.

The *Cosmography* was known in Syriac circles; witness a chapter of the *Syriac Chronicle* of 569, and the *Hexaēmeron* of Jacob of Edessa (VII-2). Much was added to it by Muslim geographers, such as al-Khwārizmī (IX-1), al-Battānī (IX-2), and many others, East and West.

The Latin translation of the Greek text was made by Giacomo d'Angelo (Jacobus Angelus) in 1409.

The growing popularity of the *Cosmography* in the fifteenth century is well illustrated by the number of incunabula. While there was no incunabula edition of the *Almagest* (excepting Regiomontanus' *Epitoma* of 1496), there were seven of the *Cosmographia* (Klebs no. 812). The first was issued by Hermann Liechtenstein (Vicenza, 1475); the first with maps by Lapis (Bologna, 1477) ;[44] facsimile copy of the edition of 1477 (Klebs no. 812.2) by Edward Lynam: *The First Engraved Atlas of the World* (26 maps, Jenkintown, George H. Beans, 1941).

The first Greek edition was prepared by no less a person than Erasmus (Basel, Froben and Episcopius, 1533).

[44] Not 1462 as printed by mistake in its colophon (*Osiris 5*, 103). First and last page of the first edition, 1475 (*Osiris 5*, 134-35).

TRADITION OF THE TETRABIBLOS

The *Tetrabiblos* must have been a popular book in Greek circles, because astrological fancies and other aberrations flourished more and more as the old culture was decaying, but the ancient tradition is obscure. An introduction to it is ascribed to Porphyrios (III-2), a paraphrase to Proclos (V-2), and there is an anonymous commentary which might also be by the latter. That is not much to go by.[45]

The *Tetrabiblos* was one of the earliest Greek books to be translated into Arabic, under al-Manṣūr (VIII-2), the second 'Abbasī caliph (754-75), the founder of Baghdād—the translator being Abū Yaḥyā al-Baṭrīq (VIII-2). Al-Baṭrīq's version was commented upon by 'Umar ibn al-Farrukhān (IX-1), and by Aḥmad ibn Yūsuf (IX-2). The *Tetrabiblos* was translated again by Ḥunain ibn Isḥāq (IX-2) and this translation was commented upon by 'Alī ibn Riḍwān (XI-1); 'Alī's commentary was much used by astrologers.

Another translation by Ibrāhīm ibn al-Ṣalt (date unknown) corrected by Thābit ibn Qurra (IX-2) and (or) Ḥunain ibn Isḥāq was Latinized by Plato of Tivoli (XII-1) and was the first Ptolemaic work to be translated into Latin. A new Latin translation was made in 1206 by an unknown scholar. The *Tetrabiblos* and 'Alī ibn Riḍwān's commentary upon it were translated into Spanish, perhaps by Judah ben Moses (XIII-2), for Alfonso el Sabio (XIII-2), and from Spanish into Latin by Aegidius of Thebaldis soon after 1256.

[45] The Greek text of the paraphrase was published with a preface by Philip Melanchthon (Basel, J. Oporinus, 1554), a Greek-Latin edition of the two other texts by Hieronymus Wolf was published a few years later (Basel, Petreius, 1559).

Still another Latin translation was prepared, c. 1305, by Simon de Bredon (XIV-1). Etc.

The Latin version from the Arabic was printed very early. There are two separate incunabula, the first by Ratdolt (Venice, 1484) and the second by Locatellus (Venice, 1493), plus many included in other incunabula editions (Klebs no. 814).

There were also Latin versions from the Greek, one being mentioned by Henry Bate of Malines (XIII-2) in 1281. The first edition of the Greek text, by Joachim Camerarius was printed by J. Petreius of Nürnberg in 1535, and reprinted by Joannes Oporinus at Basel in 1553. Both editions included Latin translations from the Greek, the first by Camerarius and the second by Philip Melanchthon; both included also the *Carpos* in Greek and Latin.

An English translation by the Dublin quack, John Whalley, was printed in London in 1701 and again in 1786. Another English translation by J. M. Ashmand in London in 1822 was reprinted there in 1917 and in Chicago in 1936 (*Isis 35*, 181).

Two critical editions of the Greek text were published independently in 1940, the one by Franz Boll and Aemilia Boer in the *Opera omnia* of Ptolemy (III, 1, Teubner, Leipzig) and the other by Frank Egleston Robbins, with an English version, in the Loeb Classical Library (reprinted in 1948; *Isis 33*, 718-19).

There are thus three English versions of the *Tetrabiblos*. Until 1952, this was the only Ptolemaic text which could be read in our language. *Horresco referens!* (*Isis 44*, 278).

10. BIBLIOGRAPHY OF PTOLEMY

1. Complete Works

Opera quae extant omnia. Edited by J. L. Heiberg (Teubner, Leipzig, 1898 f.). Vol. I in 2 vols., *Almagest* (1903). Vol. II, *Opera astronomica minora* (1907). Vol. III, 1, *Tetrabiblos* edited by Franz Boll and Aemilia Boer (1940).

This is all in Greek, except when the Greek text is lost.

2. The *Almagest*

The standard edition is Heiberg's in the *Opera omnia* (Vol. I in 2 vols, 1898-1903). The Greek-French edition by the Abbé Nicolas B. Halma with notes by J. B. J. Delambre is very convenient (2 vols., Paris, 1813-16). Facsimile reprint of smaller size (Paris, Hermann, 1927).

German translation by Karl Manitius derived from the Heiberg text (2 vols., Leipzig, 1912-13).

An English translation by Catasby Taliaferro is included in *Great Books of the Western World* (XVI, 1-478, Chicago, 1952; *Isis 44*, 278-80).

Christian H. F. Peters and Edward Ball Knobel. *Ptolemy's Catalogue of Stars. A revision of the Almagest* (208 pp., Carnegie Institution of Washington, 1915; *Isis 2*, 401).

3. The *Geography*

Ptolemaei Geographiae Codex Urbinas Graecus 82. Edited by Joseph Fischer and Pius Francus de Cavalieri (4 vols., Leiden, Brill, 1932). For fuller description and review, see *Isis 20*, 266-70). This includes an elaborate study of Ptolemy and his *Geography* by Father Fischer with indices (Tomus prodromus, pars prior, 624 pp.).

Traité de géographie traduit pour la première fois du grec en français sur les MSS de la Bibliothèque du Roi par l'abbé Halma (quarto 214 pp., Paris, 1828), not seen.

Geography of Ptolemy, translated into English by Edward Luther Stevenson (folio, 183 pp., 29 pl., New York Public

Library, 1932; *Isis 20,* 270-74; *22,* 533-39) . No index. Imperfect translation.

Let us hope that the edition of the Greek text being prepared for the *Opera Omnia* will soon appear. Thus far, we have no better edition of the Greek text than that of Carolus Müller: *Ptolemaei Geographia* (2 vols., Paris, Firmin Didot, 1883-1901), with Latin translation; but it is incomplete (stopping at vol. V, cap. 19), and hence lacks an index.

For an index, one must refer to the old Greek edition of C. F. A. Nobbe (Ed. stereotype, 3 vols., Leipzig, Tauchnitz, 1843-45) , or the old *Nomenclator* which the Fleming Abraham Ortelius (1527-98) added to his *Theatrum orbis terrarum* (Antwerp, 1579) and later editions and also published separately.

Two bibliographies may be added. Henry Newton Stevens: *Ptolemy's Geography. A Brief Account of all the Printed Editions down to 1730* (62 pp., London, Stevens and Stiles, 1908). William Harris Stahl: *Ptolemy's Geography* (86 pp., New York Public Library) . This is especially useful to find studies devoted to the Ptolemaic account of specific regions, say, Sicily or Ceylon.

4. *Alia*

For editions of the *Optics* or *Tetrabiblos,* see chapters 7-8 above devoted to these books. For additional bibliography, see my *Introduction* (*1,* 274-78) and the Critical Bibliographies of *Isis,* section II-1.

THE END OF GREEK SCIENCE AND CULTURE

(from c. 300 to 529)

LEAVING out of the question prehistoric times, which cannot be measured, Greek culture begins with Homer (say, in the ninth or eighth centuries); Greek science begins a little later with Thalēs and Pythagoras (sixth century). My first lecture on Euclid (c. 300 B.C.) dealt with a relatively late stage of Greek culture, the so-called Hellenistic. In order to deal with Ptolemy in my second lecture, we had to make a jump of more than four centuries; we shall now consider a period which begins 150 years and ends 350 years later. This illustrates once more the length of ancient Greek culture, its duration and its inexhaustible variety. The Roman world of Ptolemy was very different from the Alexandrian of Euclid and the world which I shall try to evoke here is again extremely different.

The Roman Empire and Christianity were born at about the same time. By the beginning of the fourth century the Roman Empire was going down rapidly while Christianity was going up, and we witness the symbiosis of the old Pagan moving slowly to his death and of the Christian youth preparing to live and conquer.

This lecture will be divided into three parts: Greek mathetics, Greek medicine, and the philosophical and religious background. My reason for speaking of the background in the last part instead of the first will be apparent later on.

1. GREEK MATHEMATICIANS

Ptolemy's gigantic efforts were followed by a lull of more than a century. So much so that when the next great mathematician appeared he felt obliged to prepare a summary of earlier books, under the title *Mathematical Collection* (*synagōgē*). This mathematician was Pappos of Alexandria. According to a scholion (marginal note) in an old manuscript, he lived under Diocletian (emperor, 284-305) and therefore it is tempting to consider him a man of the third century like the algebraist Diophantos,[1] but according to Canon Rome[2] Pappos' commentary on the *Almagest* was probably written after 320 and the *Mathematical Collection* even later. Pappos wrote various commentaries on Euclid and Ptolemy, but his

[1] That was done in my *Introduction*, where Pappos was placed in the time of Diophantos (III-2). It would have been better, perhaps, to place him in (IV-1) (*Intro. 3*, ix). Pappos would seem to be half-way between Diophantos and Theōn of Alexandria.

[2] Adolphe Rome: "Sur la date de Pappus" (*Annales de la Société scientifique de Bruxelles*, serie A [1927], 46-48), *Isis 11*, 415-16.

main work is the *Synagōgē* already mentioned, of which a great part has come down to us. It is divided into eight books; we have everything except Book I and chapters 1 to 13 of Book II, the preface to IV, and perhaps the end of VIII. It is difficult to analyze it because it is devoted to a multiplicity of mathematical subjects and combines for most of them old and new. Pappos was not a teacher like Euclid or Ptolemy but a learned man who was familiar with the whole of Greek mathematics and tried to summarize it in his own peculiar way. He was a good commentator because he was on a level with his greatest predecessors and was able to add ingenious theorems and problems of his own, but he was not very methodical. As far as we understand the general composition of his *Synagōgē*, he had taken notes on the mathematical classics, invented and solved new problems, and then classified them in eight books. Each book is preceded by general reflections which give to that group of problems its philosophical, mathematical and historical setting. These prefaces are of deep interest to historians of mathematics and, therefore, it is a great pity that three of them are lost (the prefaces to Books I, II and IV). They may turn up some day in an Arabic version.

The following notes will indicate roughly the contents of the *Synagōgē*, book by book.

Book II (chapters 14-16). Commentary on Apollōnios' method for the writing of large numbers in terms of powers of myriads ($10,000^n$) and for operating with them.

Book III. History of the problem: to find two mean proportionals in continued proportion between two given straight lines. Classification of geometrical problems in three classes (1) plane, (2) solid, (3) those requiring the use of higher curves for their solution. Curious propositions suggested by the paradoxes of Erycinos (otherwise unknown). How to inscribe the five regular solids in a given sphere.

Book IV. Extension of the Pythagorean problem on the square of the hypotenuse. Circles inscribed in the arbēlos (semicircular knife used by cobblers), commentary on a book of Archimēdēs (lost in Greek, preserved in Arabic). Discussion of Archimēdēs' spiral, Nicomēdēs' conchoid, the quadratrix, spherical spiral. Trisection of any angle, etc. This includes a method of integration (for the spiral) different from that of Archimēdēs.

Book V. Isoperimetry, derived from Zēnodōros (II-1 B.C.). The delightful preface refers to the bees whose cells are built with a great regularity and a marvelous economy of space. Pappos did not deal only with plane problems; he also stated that the sphere has the greatest volume for a given surface.

Book VI, mainly astronomical, being inspired by some of the authors of the "little astronomy," Autolycos (IV-2 B.C.), Aristarchos (III-1 B.C.), Euclid (III-1 B.C.), Theodosios (I-1 B.C.) and Menelaos (I-2).[3]

Book VII is by far the longest book of the collection; the longest books next to it are III, IV and V, but VII is almost as long as these three books put together. It is also the most important for historians, because it discusses a good many lost books of Aristaios (IV-2 B.C.), Euclid, Apollōnios, and

---

[3] The "little astronomy" or *ho micros astronomumenos* (*topos*) was so called perhaps by contrast with the *megalē syntaxis*. Many of these writings were transmitted together (in the same manuscripts) to Greek readers and later to Arabic ones. The Arabic collection, including the Greek texts plus some original Arabic ones, was called *Kitāb al-mutawassiṭāt bain al-handasa wal-hai'a*, The middle books between geometry and astronomy (*Intro. 2*, 1001).

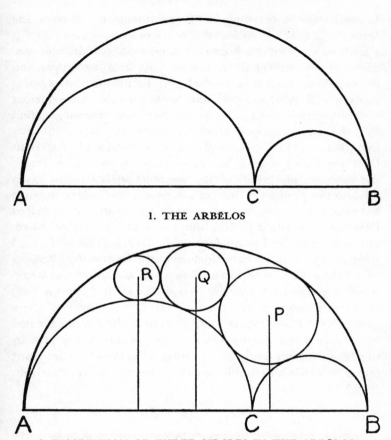

1. THE ARBĒLOS

2. INSCRIPTION OF THREE CIRCLES IN THE ARBĒLOS

If P, Q, R are the centers of these circles, d_1, d_2, d_3 their diameters, P_1, P_2, p_3 the distances of the centers to the base line, then $p_1 = d_1 p_2 = 2 d_2 p_3 = 3 d_3 p_4 = $ etc.

From Heath: *Manual of Greek Mathematics*, Oxford, 1931, p. 442; *Isis* *16*, 450.

Eratosthenēs.[4] According to its own title, it contains the lēmmata of the "solved locus" (*ho topos analyomenos*), and is a kind of textbook on geometrical method for advanced students. It was dedicated (as well as Book VIII) to Pappos' son Hermodōros. After a preface wherein he defines and explains analysis and synthesis, he deals with each of those ancient treatises, stressing one point or another. For example, we find in it the famous Pappos' problem: "given several straight lines in a plane, to find the locus of a point, such that when straight lines are drawn from it to the given lines at a given angle, the products of certain of the segments shall be in a given ratio to the product of the remaining ones." This problem is important in itself, but even more so because it exercized Descartes' mind and caused him to invent the method of co-ordinates explained in his *Géométrie* (1637). Think of a seed lying asleep for more than thirteen centuries and then helping to produce that magnificent flowering, analytical geometry. Another proposition was the seed of the centrobaric method; it proves a theorem equivalent to the Guldin theorem: "if a plane closed curve rotates around an axis, the volume created by its revolution will be equal to the product of the area by the length of the path of its center of gravity." The Jesuit father Paul Guldin published that theorem more clearly in 1640.[5]

[4] No less than twelve treatises in 33 books, most of them by Euclid (3 treatises in 6 books) and Apollōnios (7 treatises in 20 books).

[5] The Guldin anticipation in Pappos is imperfect and perhaps an interpolation; it does not occur in all the manuscripts. Guldin expressed the theorem very clearly for the first time but his proof is incomplete. The first complete proof was given by his adversary, Bonaventura Cavalieri, in 1647.

Another problem bearing Pappos' name is *not* in his *Collection,* however. Given a point A on the bisectrix of a given angle, to draw through A, a segment *a* ending on both sides of the angle. This problem had an extraordinary fortune, probably because of this singularity: it leads to an equation of the 4th degree and yet can be solved with ruler and compass.[6]

The most astonishing part of that Book VII has not yet been mentioned. Dealing with the lost treatise of Apollōnios on the determinate section (*diōrismenē tomē*), Pappos explains the involution of points.

The final Book VIII is mechanical and is largely derived from Hērōn of Alexandria. Following Hērōn, Pappos distinguished various parts of theoretical mechanics (geometry, arithmetic, astronomy and physics) and a practical or manual part. This book may be considered the climax of Greek mechanics and helps us to realize the great variety of problems to which the Hellenistic mechanicians[7] addressed themselves. Many needs had to be filled: the moving of heavy bodies, war engines for offensive or defensive purposes, machines for the pumping of water, automata and other gadgets for the use of wonder workers; water clocks and moving spheres. Pappos was interested in practical problems, such as the construction of toothed gearings and of a cylindrical helix (*cochlias*) acting upon the teeth of a wheel, but he was even more concerned with mathematical methods, such as the finding of two mean proportionals between two given lines, the determination of

[6] A thick volume was devoted to it by A. Maroger: *Le Problème de Pappus et Ses Cent Premières Solutions* (Paris, Vuibert, 1925) , reviewed in *Revue Générale des Sciences* (37, 338) .

[7] Pappos knew them chiefly through Hērōn; Philōn is quoted only a few times, Ctēsibios not at all.

centers of gravity, the drawing of a conic through five given points. The mathematician in him was so keen that he was trying to solve theoretical problems such as this one: how to fill the area of a circle with seven equal regular hexagons.

If Book VIII is the climax of Greek mechanics, we may say as well that the whole *Collection* is a treasury and to some extent the culmination of Greek mathematics. Little was added to it in the Byzantine age and the Western world, having lost its knowledge of Greek together with its interest in higher mathematics, was not able to avail itself of the riches which Pappos had put together. The ideas collected or invented by Pappos did not stimulate Western mathematicians until very late, but when they finally did, they caused the birth of modern mathematics—analytical geometry, projective geometry, centrobaric method. That birth or rebirth, from Pappos' ashes, occurred within four years (1637-40). Thus was modern geometry connected immediately with the ancient one as if nothing had happened between.

Pappos was the greatest mathematician of the final period of ancient science, and no one emulated him in Byzantine times. He was the last mathematical giant of antiquity. Nevertheless, he was followed by a very distinguished group of mathematicians, so numerous indeed that it will not be possible to speak of each of them except in the briefest manner. Serēnos of Antinoopolis (IV-1) was another Egyptian Greek, hailing from the city in Middle Egypt which Hadrian had founded in memory of the beautiful Antinoos, drowned in the Nile in 122. We must assume that Serēnos studied or flourished in Alexandria, and in any case he was in touch with the Alexandrian school, the greatest mathematical school of his age as well as the one which was nearest to him. He wrote a commentary on the *Conics* of Apollōnios and two original treatises on the sections of cylinders and cones.

And now let us consider two other illustrious Alexandrians, father and daughter, Theōn (IV-2) and Hypatia (V-1), both teachers in the Museum. Theōn edited Euclid's *Elements* and wrote a very elaborate commentary on the *Almagest*. He completed Ptolemy's establishment of sexagesimal fractions; Hypatia revised her father's commentary on Books III and following of the *Almagest* and she may be responsible for a new method of sexagesimal division closer to the Babylonian than her father's, but it is impossible to know exactly what belongs to either of them. Her own commentaries on Apollōnios, Ptolemy's *Canōn* (chronology) and Diophantos are all lost, but she is immortalized by the grateful letters of Synesios of Cyrēnē (V-1) [8] and, above all, by her martyrdom in 415. She enjoys the double honor of being the first female mathematician and one of the first martyrs of science.

After Hypatia's death, there was a lull in the mathematical (pagan) school of Alexandria, and no wonder. The next leaders belong to the following century, Ammōnios and Philoponos. Ammōnios, son of Hermias (VI-1), studied under Proclos in Athens, but he restored the school of Alexandria and, judging by the merit of some of his pupils, must have

---

[8] Synesios of Cyrēnē (c. 370—c. 413) was converted in middle age (c. 407) and became soon afterward bishop of Ptolemais (410), one of the five cities of Cyrenaica (Pentapolis). Of his letters 159 have been preserved, dating from 394 to 413; seven are addressed to Hypatia covering the same lapse of time. In letter 15, he asked her to have a baryllion (a kind of hydrometer) made for him. This is the first description of that instrument in literature, but its use is such an obvious application of Archimedian hydrostatics that some Hellenistic mechanician had probably invented it long before the fifth century.

been a great teacher. He divided mathematics into four branches: arithmetic, geometry, astronomy, music—a division which became in the Latin world the quadrivium.[9] His disciple, Joannes Philoponos (VI-1),[10] was primarily a philosopher, but he wrote the earliest treatise on the astrolabe and a commentary on the arithmetic of Nicomachos.

Now, let us return to Athens. When it had become a provincial city of the Roman empire, its schools were eclipsed by the Museum, yet it continued to be the sacred metropolis of Hellenism. Political and commercial power had withdrawn, but philosophy had remained. Yet, it must be admitted that by the end of the fourth century, only one of the four main schools was really alive. We cannot name the headmasters or leaders of the Aristotelian, Stoic and Epicurean schools. Only in the Academy was the succession (*diadochē*) of the headmasters preserved. Let us name them for the sake of curiosity: Priscos (c. 370), Plutarchos, son of Nestorios[11] (d. 431), Syrianos of Alexandria (V-1), Domninos of Larissa (V-2), Proclos the Successor (V-2), Marinos of Sichem (V-2), Isidōros of Alexandria, Hēgias, Zēnodotos, and finally Damascios (VI-1).

[9] The word *quadrivium* was introduced by Ammōnios' Latin contemporary, Boetius (VI-1), but the idea is considerably older. It was adumbrated by Archytas of Tarentum (IV-1 B.C.), for whom see my *History of Science* (pp. 434, 440, 521).

[10] Joannes Philoponos is identical with John the Grammarian (*Intro. 1*, 421, 480). He was a Jacobite Christian and one of the very greatest personalities of his age (*Isis 18*, 447).

[11] The decadence of the age is illustrated by the fact that this Plutarchos was called the Great! Plutarchos of Athens is now almost unknown. When referring to his illustrious namesake, Plutarchos of Chairōneia (I-2), I shall call the latter "Plutarch," because he belongs to world literature. Plutarchos' daughter, Asclēpigeneia, was a "femme savante," the Athenian contemporary and counterpart of the Alexandrian Hypatia.

This list suggests two remarks. First, it is probably complete[12] and thus proves a modicum of continuity, but the fact that many of the *diadochoi* are all but unknown is an ominous sign. Who were Priscos, Hēgias and Zēnodotos? As to the last head of the Academy, we do not even know his personal name, for Damascios simply means the Damascene. Second, an analysis of the list would show that the schools of Athens and Alexandria were relatively close to each other. Ammōnios was a pupil of Proclos and a teacher of Damascios; it is a regular *chassé-croisé*. Alexandrians would study in Athens and Athenians in Alexandria. Two at least of the *diadochoi* of the Academy, Syrianos and Isidōros, were Alexandrians.

It is clear that the Academy had ceased to be a high mathematical school. The majority of the teachers and students were interested only in Neoplatonic arithmetic, that is, number mysticism. However, Domninos of Larissa tried to react against that and to revive the Euclidian theory of numbers. Proclos was by far the greatest headmaster in the last century of the Academy's existence. He was of Lycian origin[13] but born at Byzantion; he studied in Alexandria, but too late to drink at the sources of Hypatia's wisdom; he went back to Athens and was head of the Academy until his death in 485. He has been called "the Hegel of Neoplatonism" by people who wanted to praise him as much as possible; he was certainly more influential as a philosopher than as an astronomer or a mathematician. Yet we owe him gratitude for his introduction to Ptolemaic astronomy and his commentary on Book I of the

[12] Ten headmasters seem enough to cover a period of 150 years.

[13] In our list of the last ten headmasters of the Academy, only seven are of known origin; six of these came from Egypt or Western Asia; only one (Plutarchos) was Athenian. Simplicios also came from the Near East.

Elements. That commentary is of considerable value for the history of Euclid's sources; much of the information which is thus conveyed to us was derived from the lost works of two Rhodians, Eudēmos (IV-2 B.C.) and Geminos (I-1 B.C.). Without Proclos, our knowledge of ancient geometry would be considerably poorer than it is.

Marinos of Sichem wrote a preface to Euclid's *Data* (exercises of geometry), but Damascios did *not* write the "XVth book of Euclid" ascribed to him.

The greatest mathematician who flourished at Athens in the sixth century has not yet been named, for he was not a headmaster of the Academy, that is, Simplicios (VI-1). His Aristotelian commentaries contain many items of mechanical and astronomical interest and he composed a commentary on Euclid I. The Cilician Simplicios and the Egyptian Philoponos were the outstanding men of science of their age.

One last remark about the Academy. From the end of the third century, it was the only philosophical school left in Athens, but that was at the price of its own integrity. The Academy had ceased for centuries to be Platonic; not only was its prevailing philosophy Neoplatonic but it gave hospitality to other philosophies and was ready to discuss them all and to syncretize them. Syrianos, Proclos, Marinos wrote commentaries on Aristotle; Simplicios wrote one on Epictētos.

In addition to the mathematical schools of Alexandria and Athens there was also in the first half of the sixth century a new school in Constantinople, illustrated by Isidōros of Milētos and his pupil Eutocios of Ascalōn, but their main activities were probably posterior to the closing of the Academy.[14] The

[14] And hence outside of the scope of this lecture. The same may be said of Philoponos and Simplicios.

Constantinopolitan mathematicians were probably Christians, not so any of the others, except Philoponos, who was a Monophysite.

We have spoken of a dozen mathematicians. Instead of considering the tradition of each of them, we shall restrict ourselves to five, Pappos, Serēnos, Theōn, Hypatia and Proclos.

The tradition of Pappos is exceptional in that it involves Armenian literature, for Moses of Chorene (V-1), who had been educated in Alexandria, wrote in Armenian a *Geography* which was based on Pappos' lost work *ad hoc*. The commentary on the *Almagest* was amplified by Theōn; his commentary on the *Elements* of Euclid was used by Proclos and Eutocios. The part of it devoted to Book X, lost in Greek, was preserved in the Arabic version of Abū 'Uthmān al-Dimishqī (X-1). Abū-l-Wafā' (X-2) derived his knowledge of the solid polyhedra from Pappos' *Collection*.

The first Greek edition of the *Almagest* (Basel, J. Walderus, 1538)[15] included Pappos' commentary to Book V.

The first printed edition of the *Collection* was the Latin translation from the Greek by Federigo Commandino (Pesaro, Hier. Concordia, 1588), reprinted in Venice, 1589, and Bologna, 1660. The first complete edition of the Greek text appeared only three centuries later; it was admirably prepared by Friedrich Hultsch (3 vols., Berlin, 1876-78).[16]

William Thomson: The Commentary of Pappos on Book X of Euclid's *Elements*, Arabic text and translation (Cambridge, Harvard, 1930; *Isis 16*, 132-36).

---

[15] Facsimile of title page in *Isis 36*, 256.

[16] Hultsch's edition was a model followed by later editors of Greek mathematical texts such as Heiberg. For Friedrich Hultsch (1833-1906), see Tannery, *Mémoires 15*, 243-317; *Isis 25*, 57-59).

Adolphe Rome: "Pappus, Commentaire sur les livres 5 ct 6 de l'Almageste" (*Studi e testi 54*, Vatican, 1931; *Isis 19*, 381), Greek text.

Paul Ver Eecke: Pappus. La Collection mathématique (2 vols., Bruges, 1933; *Isis 26*, 495), French translation.

The early tradition of Serēnos was mixed up with the Apollonian tradition in both Greek and Arabic. The first printed text was the Latin version which Federigo Commandino published in his Apollōnios (Bologna, Alex. Benatius, 1566). The first Greek edition was included in the splendid Greek-Latin edition of Apollōnios by Edmund Halley (Oxford, 1710). New Greek-Latin edition by J. L. Heiberg (Leipzig, 1896). French translation by Paul Ver Eecke (208 pp., Bruges, 1929; *Isis 15*, 397).

Theōn's commentary on the *Almagest*, as revised by his daughter Hypatia, was known to the Byzantine mathematicians Nicolaos Cabasilas (XIV-2) and Theodōros Melitēniōtēs (XIV-2). It was included in the first Greek edition of the *Almagest* (Basel, 1538). A new Greek edition, with French translation, was begun by Nicolas Halma (Paris, 1813-16). An exemplary edition of the Greek text was begun by Adolphe Rome in 1936; thus far, it extends to Books I-IV (Vatican, 1936-1943; *Isis 28*, 543; *36*, 255); the continuation is being prepared by his disciple, Joseph Mogenet.

Proclos was far more popular as a philosopher, theologian, and even as a physicist than as a mathematician, and the tradition of his many writings is very complex. We shall consider here only his mathematical work. Isaac Argyros (XIV-2) revised his commentary on the arithmetic of Nicomachos. His commentary on Euclid, Book I, was first printed in Greek in Simon Gryneus' Greek edition of Euclid (Basel, Hervagius, 1533). Latin editions were prepared by Franciscus Barocius (Padova, Gratiosus Perchacinus, 1560) and by Federigo Commandino with Euclid (Pesaro, 1572). Critical Greek edition by Gottfried Friedlein (515 pp., Leipzig, 1873). French translation by Paul Ver Eecke (396 pp., Bruges, 1948; *Isis 40*, 256).

The tradition of the final mathematical achievements of Hellenism is curious in at least two respects. In the first place, it hardly involved the Arabic detour, except in the case of Pappos. Their rediscovery was largely due to Byzantine scholars and later to Renaissance ones, with the result that Greek printed editions were anterior to the Latin ones, except in Serēnos' case. As far as the Latin tradition is concerned, the lion's share was done by Federigo Commandino of Urbino (1509-75), especially if one considers that he was the first to publish Pappos' *Collection,* the influence of which upon later mathematicians was considerable.

2. BYZANTINE MEDICINE

For the sake of simplicity it will be best to deal with only one physician, the greatest of this age,[17] Oribasios (IV-2), and we call him Byzantine rather than Greek or Hellenistic because he was a physician to the Byzantine court in Constantinople. Oribasios was born in Pergamon like his predecessor Galen (II-2), of whose fame he was the main artisan. His greatest work was a medical encyclopedia, *Iatricai synagōgai,* of such immense size that only one third of it has come down to us; the original extended to seventy books.[18] It is of great value for historians, for it has helped to preserve a good many earlier medical texts which would have been lost otherwise; its numerous quotations are always referred to their

[17] Aëtios of Amida (VI-1), Justinian's archiater, comes just after its end. For a general view of Byzantine medicine, see *Isis 42,* 150, or my Philadelphia lectures (1954).
[18] We have only Books I to XV, XXI-XXII, XXIV-XXV, XLIV-LI, with lacunas—a total of less than 27 books.

authors. Oribasios was befriended by Prince Julian,[19] became his physician, and was almost the only person to whom the latter revealed his apostasy. In 355, when Julian was made a Caesar and sent to Gaul, he took Oribasios with him. During his brief rule (361-63), he appointed him *quaestor* of Constantinople and charged him to go to Delphoi in order to consult the oracle and possibly revive its glory; that undertaking ended in failure[20] but Julian did not take it ill and continued to favor his physician. He encouraged him to write his medical encyclopedia, and when he started on his last campaign against Persia, Oribasios went with him and was with him at Antiocheia and at the moment of his death on the battlefield on 26 June, 363. It is clear that Oribasios shared the pagan faith of his master. This is sufficiently proved by the facts already mentioned but also by the persecution which he suffered after his protector's death. The Christian emperors who followed Julian the Apostate, Valens and Valentinian,

[19] Julian, born in Constantinople in 331, was but a few years younger than Oribasios, born c. 325. While he was wintering in Paris, 358-59, Julian wrote to Oribasios, then in Vienne, a letter the terms of which prove their intimacy.

[20] According to Geōrgios Cedrēnos (flourished, eleventh/twelfth century), author of a world chronicle from the Creation to 1057, the oracle of Apollōn gave this answer:

"Tell the king, on earth has fallen the glorious dwelling,
"And the watersprings that spake are quenched and dead.
"Not a cell is left the God, no roof, no cover,
"In his hand the prophet laurel flowers no more."

(Swinburne's version in *The Last Oracle*). The sacred oracle foretold the end of paganism!

If one wishes to understand how the Pythian prophetess functioned, he should read Herbert William Parke, *History of the Delphic Oracle* (Oxford, 1939; *Isis 35*, 250). A similar institution is still functioning today in Tibet and was observed and described by Heinrich Harrer, *Seven Years in Tibet* (pp. 180-82, London, 1953).

confiscated Oribasios' estates and drove him into exile. Oribasios flourished for a time at the court of barbarian (Gothic?) kings and distinguished himself so well that he was recalled to Constantinople, c. 369. His goods were restituted to him and he was permitted to continue his medical practice and writing. He died c. 400.

He is a good example of the transition between paganism and Christianity. It is possible that he had been brought up as a Christian even as Julian was, but that under the latter's ascendency his pagan feelings[21] were revived. According to Eunapios (V-1), he studied medicine under Zēnōn of Cypros,[22] and sat at the latter's feet at the Museum together with Magnos of Antiocheia, the Iatrosophist. Both Zēnōn and Magnos were pagans. Julian died too young (at thirty-two) to recant; Oribasios lived until he was about seventy-five; we may safely assume that he became a Christian again and died as such, for paganism was no longer acceptable either in the empire or in the barbarian kingdoms. His son Eustathios, to whom his *Synopsis* is dedicated, was a Christian and a friend of St. Basil (IV-2).

The purpose of Oribasios' *Medical Collection* is so well ex-

[21] The word *feelings* is the correct one, for the main cause of attachment to paganism was not rational but sentimental, the love of the ancient cult and liturgy. The situation is similar to that of Catholics who become Protestants, but in the course of time cannot bear any longer the loss of sacramental aids and of the sacred liturgy and music, and return to their original faith.

[22] Zēnōn was eventually driven out of the Museum by Geōrgios of Cappadocia (Arian bishop of Alexandria, 356-61) but reinstated by Julian. The founder of Stoicism, Zēnōn of Cition (IV-2 B.C.) is sometimes called Zēnōn of Cypros, but there can be no confusion between two men separated by seven centuries.

plained at the beginning of it that it is best to quote his own words:

> Autocratōr Iulian, I have completed during our stay in Western[23] Gaul the medical summary which your Divinity had commanded me to prepare and which I have drawn exclusively from the writings of Galen. After having praised it, you commanded me to search for and put together all that is most important in the best medical books and all that has contributed to attain the medical purpose. I gladly undertook that work, being convinced that such a collection would be very useful. . . . As it would be superfluous and even absurd to quote from the authors who have written in the best manner and then again from those who have not written as carefully, I shall take my materials exclusively from the best authors, without omitting anything which I first obtained from Galen, and I shall adapt my own compilation to the fact of his superiority; Galen used the best methods and the most exact definitions, because he follows the Hippocratic principles and opinions. I shall adopt the following order: hygiene and therapeutics, man's nature and structure; conservation of health and its restoration, diagnosis and prognosis; correction of diseases and symptoms, etc.

My rough translation of the preface tells us the essential: Julian was really Oribasios' patron and animator, and Galen was the main source, to which every other source was subordinated. Galen's perfection was ascribed partly to the excellence of his own source, Hippocratēs. Oribasios' references to Galen are innumerable and his praise of him so frequent

---

[23] Western Gaul as opposed to Eastern Gaul or Galatia in Anatolia, with which Oribasios and Julian were more familiar. As Oribasios completed his summary in Gaul, we may assume that part of it at least was written in Paris.

and emphatic that it established Galen's superiority as a kind of medical dogma.

The books of the *Synagōgai* which have come down to us are Book I, 1-65, II, 1-27, Plant foods. II, 28-58, Animal foods; 59-69, Milk, cheese, honey, horse flesh and flesh of other solipeds, generalities. III, Various kinds of foods, divided according to their physiological properties. IV, Preparation of various kinds of food. V, Beverages. VI, Physical exercises. VII, 1-22, Bloodletting. VII, 23-26, VIII, Purgatives, diuretics, emetics, hemagogues. IX, 1-20, Air, climates of various localities. IX, 21-55, External remedies, such as fomentations, cataplasms, poultices, embrocations, cupping. X, 1-9, Water, sand and air baths. X, 10-42, External remedies. XI-XIII, *Materia medica* (copied verbatim from Dioscoridēs but in alphabetical order). XIV-XV, Simple drugs. XVI (only a short fragment), Composite drugs. (XVI-XX lost.) XXI. Elements and temperaments. XXII, Generation (XXIII lost.) XXIV, Internal organs, from the brain to the sexual parts. XXV, Anatomical nomenclature, Bones and muscles (57 chapters), Nerves and vessels (4 chapters) .

XLIV, Inflammations, tumors, abscesses, fistulae, gangrene, erysipelas, herpes, boils. XLV, Tumors. XLVI, Fractures. XLVII, Dislocations. XLVIII, Slings and bandages. XLIX, Apparatus used to reduce luxations. L, Genitourinary troubles, Hernias. LI, Ulcers. (LII-LXX are lost.)

These books plus fragments from the lost ones were edited in Greek and French by Ulco Cats Bussemaker and Charles Victor Daremberg in four thick volumes (Paris, 1851-62). Two more volumes of the same magnificent edition were published posthumously by Auguste Molinier. Vol. 5 (1873) contains Oribasios' *Synopsis*[24] (medical summary) in nine books dedicated to his son Eustathios, and his *Euporista* (*Remedia parabilia,* home medicine) in four books dedicated to Eunapios, plus ancient Latin versions of the *Synopsis* and Latin additions to the Greek text. Vol. 6 (1876) contains more ancient Latin versions of the *Synopsis* and *Euporista* and an elaborate index to the six volumes.

It is well nigh impossible to assess the intrinisic merits of such a bulky legacy as Oribasios' is. It gives us a clear idea of the medical experience available in the second half of the fourth century; that experience and knowledge were essentially of pagan origin, and we may call Oribasios the last of the pagan doctors as well as the first of the Byzantine age.

The Oribasios tradition was triple—Latin, Greek and Arabic. The Latin versions edited by Molinier (1873-76) go back, some of them, to the sixth century; the earliest were made in Ravenna during the Ostrogothic period (489-554); others were made in the seventh and eighth centuries. These Latin versions have transmitted to us parts of the text lost in the original Greek. They were made when Oribasios was relatively modern and when relations between the Latin and Greek worlds were still frequent.

The main tradition was Greek, however; the other Byzantine physicians Aëtios of Amida (VI-1), Alexandros of

[24] Would this be a revised edition of the summary which Oribasios completed for Julian in Gaul before the compilation of his *Synagōgai?* See Oribasios' preface quoted above.

94

Tralleis (VI-2), Paulos of Aigina (VII-1), etc., were to some extent dependent upon it.

The Arabic tradition, instead of being anterior to the Latin and the basis of it, was much posterior. The only Arabic versions of Oribasios were made by ʿĪsā ibn Yaḥyā (IX-2) and perhaps by Stephanos, son of Basileios (IX-2). The Arabs paid more attention to Aëtios, Alexandros, and especially to Paulos than to Oribasios, and even more to the latter's sources, Hippocratēs and Galen. Galen's extraordinary fame was built up gradually by Oribasios, by the other Byzantine physicians, by the Arabic ones and by Latin doctors of the thirteen century and later; it reached its natural culmination during the Renaissance.

There are no incunabula editions, but a number of Latin editions appeared in the sixteenth century. Most of them were restricted to a part of his writings but Giovanni Battista Rasario attempted to publish the *Opera omnia* (Basel, Isingrinius, 1557) ; reprinted in Paris, 1567. Greek editions were fewer in number in the sixteenth century, partial and small. The largest of the early Greek-Latin editions (Books I to XV of the *Collection*) was prepared by Christian Friedrich de Matthaei and published by the Imperial University of Moscow (1808). The first complete edition of the Greek text (as complete as it could be) was the Greek-French edition of Bussemaker, Daremberg and Molinier (6 vols., Paris, 1851-76), which has already been mentioned, because it is the most convenient. A more critical edition of the Greek text is included in the *Corpus Medicorum Graecorum*, Part VI, the *Opera Omnia* edited by Joannes Raeder (1926-33). General indices are being prepared by M. Haesler; in the meanwhile, the Greek-French edition is indispensable.

3. THE PHILOSOPHIC AND RELIGIOUS BACKGROUND

The reader may be astonished by the fact that most of the men of science of whom I have spoken were pagans (or were pagans most of the time) and exclaim, "How could that be after more than three or four centuries of missionary efforts?" The situation was extremely complex.[25] Philosophical teaching continued; that teaching was essentially pagan, restricted to Neoplatonism and mixed up with various forms of mysticism. Stoicism was very strong but was also befouled with superstitions.

The old mythology had become untenable, but the mysteries, cults and liturgies were still popular among all classes. As far as the educated and sophisticated people were concerned, the myths were treasured only as a form of national poetry but had been otherwise replaced by the astral religion, which favored astrological delusions and was in turn fostered by them. This was much too learned and too objective for the common men and women who craved a living faith and a religion which was personal, emotional, and colorful. Those cravings were satisfied in varying degrees by a number of oriental religions,[26] of which Christianity was for a long time the least conspicuous. The development of Christianity, early and late, is one of the mysteries of the world; it is the sacred mystery in the highest sense. The events which guided the Church and caused its final triumph in the face of innumerable calamities are so incredible, or call them miraculous, that

[25] The following discussion concerns only the Greek world, and this means southeastern Europe and the Near East.

[26] Masterly account of them by Franz Cumont, *Les religions Orientales dans le Paganisme Romain* (4th ed., Paris, Geuthner, 1929; *Isis 15*, 271).

Christian apologists have used them as clinching proofs of the truth and superiority of their faith.

One of the most astonishing factors is the pre-eminence in the earliest times of the poorest people, those who were despised and downtrodden. The men who had the least amount of social influence were the main agents of the revolution which changed the whole world. It was only later and very gradually that men of substance joined the catechumens. That story is so well known that I need not repeat it here. Let us make a big jump to the time which we are now contemplating. It was beautifully introduced by a woman of humble parentage, the daughter, it is said, of an innkeeper, Helenē, who became the mistress of Constantios, a Roman officer. A child was born to them at York, c. 274, named Constantine, and the parents were then duly married, but when Constantios was elevated to the Caesarship in 292, he was obliged to put her aside in order to marry one who was more respectable. Constantios Chlōros was emperor from 305 to 306, his son Constantine the Great, from 306 to 337.

Constantine was the first emperor to support Christianity. In 313, he issued the Edict of Milan, securing toleration for the Christians throughout the empire, and the official recognition of Christendom occurred soon afterward. By 324, Christian monograms became prominent on the coinage. Constantine moved his capital away from Rome which was still a stronghold of paganism and established it in 326 on the site of Byzantion; the new city was called after himself, Constantinople, inaugurated in 330 and dedicated to the Holy Virgin. Constantine was called the Great; he was really a little man, but he saw visions and took momentous decisions; he caused the political success of Christianity and the relega-

97

tion of paganism, and he elaborated the comprehensive and absolute authority of the Autocratōr in church and state. His many sins and crimes were washed away when he was baptized by Eusebios of Caisareia (IV-1) not long before his death, which occurred near Nicomēdeia in 337; he was buried in his own city, Constantinople.

It is possible that Constantine called his mother to the imperial court in or after 306, and that after his own conversion to Christianity in 312 he converted her (it is also said that it was she who converted him). Various crimes committed by Constantine were probably the cause of her vow, when already eighty years old, to make a pilgrimage to the Holy Land. She accomplished the pilgrimage and discovered the True Cross in Jerusalem, on the third of May, 326.[27] She died not long afterwards, say in 327 or 328 (in Rome?); the places of death and burial are not known. She never was an empress, even for a short time, but was eventually canonized forever.

After Constantine's death in 337, his three sons ordered the murder of other members of the imperial family, but two of his nephews, the brothers Gallos and Julian were spared. The younger one, Julian, who interests us more deeply, was born in Constantinople in 331. After his mother's untimely death, he was put under the care of Eusebios, bishop of Nicomēdeia,[28]

---

[27] The feast of the Invention of the Cross (*Inventio S. Crucis*) is celebrated on May 3. It is given far more importance by the Orthodox churches than by the Catholic or Anglican.

[28] Not to confuse Eusebios of Nicomēdeia (d. 343) with Eusebios of Caisareia (c. 265-340), the historian, he who baptized Constantine the Great *in extremis*. They were close contemporaries and both attended the Council of Nicaia (325). Julian refers to the latter in his *Letter to the Galilaeans*.

one of the most active defenders of Arianism. When Eusebios
died in 343, Julian was sent by the emperor to a castle in the
highlands of Cappadocia, where he remained six years in
solitary confinement. When his elder brother, Gallos, was
appointed Caesar in 351,[29] Julian was permitted to return to
Constantinople, where he continued his Hellenic and Christian studies. Soon afterwards, he was sent to Nicomēdeia,
where he acted as lector (*anagnōstēs*) in the local churches,
yet was friendly with the sophist Libanios, whose lectures he
had been forbidden to attend. A little later, he went to
Pergamon, then to Ephesos to commune with Maximos, Neoplatonic wonderworker and theurgist (*thaumaturgos, theurgos*),
and it was probably in that sacred city that his apostasy was
completed. Julian was initiated to Mithraism[30] about the
year 352, for he wrote in one of his letters that he had been a
Christian until his twentieth year;[31] his apostasy was kept
secret, however, for ten years. The confusion of his mind is
shown by the fact that being in Athens in 355, he followed lectures of the Christian teacher Prohairesios (St. Gregory Nazianzen and St. Basil being possibly among his classmates) and yet
was initiated to the Eleusinian mysteries. In the same year,
355, he was raised to the rank of Caesar in Milano and then
ordered to Gaul to drive out the German invaders; in the

[29] Gallos did not enjoy the Caesarship very long, for he was executed
by imperial order in 354.
[30] The Persian god Mithras had been identified with Hēlios, Sol
invictus. Joseph Bidez has shown that Mithraist influences had been
operating in Julian's family, beginning with his grandfather, Constantios
Chlōros. Therefore, Julian fancied that he was a descendant of Hēlios.
This helps to understand his apostasy. J. Bidez, "Julien l'Apostat" (*Revue
de l'instruction publique 57* [1914], 97-125, Bruxelles).
[31] Letter 47 to the Alexandrians, 434 D (Loeb ed., *3,* 149) .

course of that campaign he was able to redeem some 20,000 Gallic prisoners. Julian proved himself to be a good soldier, a clever general and a capable administrator; he did so well indeed that the emperor took umbrage at him and tried, in 360, to withdraw part of his army, but the soldiers raised Julian on their shields and nominated him their emperor. In January 361, he attended the feast of the Epiphany in Vienne (on the Rhône), then moved his army across Europe. During his passage through Naisos[32] in the same year he addressed to the Roman Senate and to the peoples of Sparta, Corinth and Athens manifestoes proclaiming the revival of the Hellenic religion. The rival emperor, Constantios, died and Julian entered Constantinople as sole emperor at the very end of the year. In the following year (362), he began his fateful campaign against the Persians and was killed on the battlefield, somewhere east of the Tigris, on 26 June 363, at the age of thirty-two.

Julian had been all his life, with increasing fervor, an enthusiastic lover of Hellenism; he was initiated into various Greek and oriental mysteries, but as soon as he found himself a soldier in the field he gave his full devotion to Mithras, who was the favorite god of the Roman legions. On 4 February 362, he proclaimed religious freedom[33] and ordered the restoration of the temples. He showed friendliness to the Jews, restored Jerusalem to them and permitted them to rebuild the "Temple of the most high God"; the building had

[32] Naisos or Nissa, Nish in eastern Yugoslavia, the very birthplace of Constantine the Great in 306.

[33] Julian's edict of toleration of 362 was the counterpart of Constantine's edict of half a century before (313), but Constantine asked freedom of religion for the Christians and Julian for the pagans. Constantine's edict was slanted against the pagans, Julian's against the Christians.

100

soon to be stopped, however, because of the earthquakes of the winter 362-63 and of the Persian war. Julian tried to be, if not impartial, at least tolerant, but as resistance to his proselytism increased, he became impatient and more and more intolerant. He gave special privileges to the pagans and withdrew those which Christians had enjoyed. The main troubles were caused by his efforts to suppress or restrict Christian education. He would have liked to avoid violence, but the old pagans who had never been Christians except in name, if at all, as soon as they escaped Christian persecution, naturally abused their new freedom and began their own destruction of men and properties. One of their outstanding victims was Geōrgios of Cappadocia,[34] the Arian bishop of Alexandria, against whom great savings of hatred had accumulated because of his own persecutions. He ventured to build a new church upon the ruins of a Mithraion and infuriated the populace; he was murdered and his body ignominiously handled by the crazy mob. This happened on 24 December 361, that is, on the eve of the Mithriac feast, *Natalis invicti,* now replaced by our Christmas.

[34] In the *Decline and Fall* (chap. 23), Gibbon speaks very harshly of him, concluding, "The odious stranger, disguising every circumstance of time and place, assumed the mask of a martyr, a saint, and a Christian hero, and the infamous George of Cappadocia has been transformed into the renowned St. George of England, the patron of arms, of chivalry and of the garter." Gibbon confused two different martyrs, Catholic and Arian. St. George of England or George the Martyr, probably an officer in Diocletian's army, was beheaded at Nicomēdeia in 303, when Arianism did not yet exist (Areios began to teach his doctrine c. 318). George of Cappadocia was an Arian; it is interesting to note that Julian seems to have had more to do with Arians, as friends or adversaries, than with Catholics.

As soon as Julian heard of this atrocious murder, he wrote two letters (from Constantinople, January 362), one to the Alexandrians to rebuke them mildly (he gave them "an advice and arguments," *parainesin cai logus*), the other to the Prefect of Egypt, demanding Geōrgios' library, which he had had occasion to use in his youth. This second letter does not contain a word of regret or of blame for the murders. It is disgraceful.

It is clear that in the end Julian's mind was distorted by violent anti-Christian prejudices, yet he was, or had been, a very intelligent man of superior morality. This is remarkable, if one remembers the terrible vicissitudes of his life.[35]

The last words ascribed to him, *necicēcas Galilaie* (Thou hast conquered, o Galileian), are legendary and paradoxical, for he died at the head of an army which must have included many Christian soldiers. The defeat of a Byzantine army by Persian barbarians was a defeat for the empire which was still, in spite of Julian's apostasy, a Christian empire.

Bibliography of Julian

Greek-Latin edition of Julian's works, *Quae extant omnia* by Petrus Martinius and Carolus Cantoclarus, i.e., Pierre Martini and Charles de Chanteclair (4 parts in 1 vol., Paris, Duvallius, 1583).

The works of Julian were edited in Greek by Friedrich Carl Hertlein (2 vols., Teubner, Leipzig, 1875-76), in Greek

---

[35] The vicissitudes of Julian's life were so strange and momentous that they soon became legendary. Richard Förster, "Kaiser Julian in der Dichtung alter und neuer Zeit" (*Studien zur vergleichenden Literaturgeschichte 5*, 1-120, Berlin, 1905). As to the modern literature inspired by Julian's fate, it will suffice to recall the names of Voltaire, Alfred de Vigny, Ibsen and Merezhkovski.

and English by Mrs. Wilmer Cave Wright[36] (Loeb Library, 3 vols., 1913-23); in Greek and French by Joseph Bidez (Assoc. Guillaume Budé, Paris, 1924 ff., *Isis 7*, 534) .

For the very interesting Syriac legend, see Georg Hoffmann, *Julianos der Abtrünnige, Syrische Erzählungen* (Leiden, 1880). Richard J. H. Gottheil: "A selection from the Syriac Julian romance, with complete glossary in English and German" (*Semitic Study Series, no. 7*, 112 pp., Leiden, 1906). Sir Hermann Gollancz, *Julian the Apostate,* now translated for the first time from the Syriac original (the only known manuscript in the British Museum, edited by Hoffmann of Kiel) (264 pp., London, 1928).

It is impossible to know how much the Greek people were influenced by Julian's apostasy. How many of them were unregenerated pagans, how many converted ones, how many born Christians? How many temples had continued to function, openly or secretly, before Julian's rule? How many churches or monasteries were closed during it? The rule was too short to do irreparable harm.

The period of Julian's life was one of great theological activity because of the existence of various heresies. Not only that, but one of the heresies, Arianism, was orthodoxy itself during the greatest part of that time. It was condemned by the Council of Nicaia,[37] 325, then again by the Council of Constantinople, 381; yet after the death of Constantine in 337, it became the orthodox doctrine and remained so, roughly, until 378. To be more precise, out of the fifty-six years

[36] Professor in Bryn Mawr, died 1951 (*Isis 43*, 368).

[37] Nicaia (= Nice, Isnik) was not far from Nicomēdea, so often mentioned above. These were the two leading cities of Bithynia, disputing the title of metropolis. Nicomēdeia is at the east end of the Propontis (Sea of Marmara), Nicaia at the east end of Lake Ascania, south of Nicomēdeia.

separating the first two councils of the Church, forty were years of Arian ascendency. Ulfilas, apostle of the Goths, was consecrated bishop by Eusebios of Nicomēdeia in 341, during the Arian supremacy, and therefore the Gothic and other Germanic tribes remained Arian for centuries.

Yet, the Catholic doctrine was very ably defended by the Nicene and post-Nicene Fathers of the Church. Of the ten generally mentioned,[38] no less than nine lived or began to live during Julian's life. They are St. Athanasios of Alexandria (d. 373), St. Basil of Cappadocia (d. 379), St. Gregory of Nazianzos (d. 389), St. Gregory of Nyssa (d. 395), St. Ambrose of Treves (d. 397), St. Epiphanios of Palestine (d. 403), St. John Chrysostom of Antioch (d. 407), St. Jerome of Dalmatia (d. 420), St. Augustine of Tagaste (d. 430). (The tenth one, St. Cyril of Alexandria, was born only in 376, many years after Julian's death; we shall come across him presently). All of these Fathers were Greek, except three of them, Ambrose, Jerome and Augustine. Julian was well acquainted with at least three of the Fathers, Athanasios, Basil and Gregory Nazianzen. Athanasios was the main opponent of Arianism from the beginning, and his life is the best symbol of the ecclesiastical vicissitudes of that turbulent age. He was bishop of Alexandria for forty-seven years, but spent about twenty years away from his see, being exiled or driven into hiding five times. We have recalled above that at the time of Julian's accession, the very see of Alexandria was held by an Arian bishop, Geōrgios of Cappadocia (bishop of Alexandria from 356 to 361).

It is noteworthy that in spite of the fact that the Empire

---

[38] E.g., in my *Introduction* (3, viii).

had become Christian soon after 313, the pagan schools continued to function, chiefly, the Academy of Athens and the
Museum of Alexandria. The Christians had their own schools,
but none had yet obtained a prestige comparable to that which
the pagan institutions enjoyed. In Alexandria, an ambitious
Christian school, the Didascaleion, had been made illustrious
by Clement of Alexandria (150-220) and Origen (III-1), but
it is doubtful whether it still flourished in the end of the fourth
century. The Museum, however, was thriving, and we have
already spoken of two illustrious teachers, Theōn and his
daughter, Hypatia, the leading mathematicians of their time.
St. Cyril, who became bishop of Alexandria in 412, decided to
put an end to pagan and Jewish learning. He persecuted the
Jews and drove them out of the city. It was during his rule
that Hypatia was murdered by a Christian mob in 415. She
was dragged into a Christian church, entirely divested and her
body torn to pieces. Cyril died in 444, was canonized by Leo
XIII and proclaimed a Doctor of the Church.[39]

Julian's apostasy and Hypatia's martyrdom are two drama-
tic events of very great significance, but we must be careful
not to misunderstand them as has been done repeatedly by
anti-clerical writers. Neither of them was a champion of free
thought. Julian was a Mithraist and a passionate defender of
Hellenism; his revival of paganism was a very queer one because it involved oriental religions of which the ancient Greeks
knew but little or nothing. He was a pagan mystic who ignored

[39] St. Cyril of Alexandria (376-444) should not be confused with his
elder contemporary, St. Cyril of Jerusalem (c. 315-86), who was Patriarch
of Jerusalem in 350, but was driven out by the Arians; he was permitted
to return to Jerusalem only in 379, and died there in 386. He took part
in the Council of Constantinople in 381.

the best part of rational Hellenism. It would not be fair to reproach him for his neglect of Greek science, but even in the field of morality, he was not well acquainted with the best thought or did not understand it. He admired equally Alexander the Great and Marcus Aurelius but was very remote from both; his Persian campaign may have been inspired by the first, but he never tried to continue Marcus' effort. He liked virtue but lacked Marcus' passion for it, his deep kindness and sanctity.

As to Hypatia, she was a Neoplatonist, not in any sense a free thinker. She was very superior to Julian in that she loved science more than myths; as a scientist, she was bound to strive for objectivity and precision, while Julian was a man of letters, a mystic and a mythomaniac. Sōcratēs might be called a martyr of freedom of thought; she was rather a martyr of science, the first, or one of the first, known to us.

To understand fairly the attitude of both of them, one must realize that in their time the defense of Hellenic traditions was the best rearguard action against Christian advance; they were not so much anti-Christian as passionately Greek.

In this period of transition and spiritual travail, Hellenism tried to take a religious form, and Christianity, a philosophical one; Christianity was struggling hard to establish an ecumenical orthodoxy against heretical distortions. They could not meet, however, because it was impossible to accept Christian doctrines without Christian faith, and the Greeks were unwilling to abandon their mythological poetry, which was the very core of Hellenism.

The educated pagans and the Christians were equally capable of enthusiasm and ecstasy but their theological conceptions were utterly incompatible.

106

The general situation in the fourth and fifth centuries was this. Whatever scientific work was done in the Greco-Roman world was done chiefly, if not exclusively, by pagans. In spite of Greek and oriental cults, the Church was gaining ground steadily, but its unity was jeopardized by schisms.

The fundamental progress of the Church, without which no later progress would have been possible, was due to the generous faith of the humbler people. This is the best example throughout the ages of the essential goodness of the masses. By and by, men of substance joined the little men, and finally the princes and rulers came in, but the Christian emperors were seldom good men; none was as good as Antoninus Pius or Marcus Aurelius. In other words, even after Constantine's recognition, the Church continued to be saved and vindicated by saints and by men and women who were poor and weak rather than rich and powerful.

As soon as Christianity was officially recognized in or soon after 313, it was necessary to define the creed with greater precision, and this was the source of endless difficulties. The definition of each dogma was bound to instigate alternatives in the minds of sophisticated theologians, quarrelsome and vain, jealous of their spiritual authority. It was extremely difficult, if not impossible, to reconcile on rational grounds the notions of monotheism and Trinity; what were the relations of Jesus Christ to God and to man? Areios began to preach c. 318 that God is absolutely unique and separate and he denied the eternity and divinity of Christ. This heresy was received so favorably by many clerks that Constantine was compelled to summon the first Council at Nicaia in 325 in order to discuss it and to push it out. The Nicene Creed rejected Arianism. In spite of that, Arianism enjoyed considerable popularity, was countenanced by emperors until 378, and remained the orthodox doctrine of the Teutonic tribes for centuries. It is very remarkable that that heresy, the first great one, was so bold that the sixteenth century Socinianism and later Unitarianism may be considered as stemming from it.

Arianism was condemned again by the second Council in Constantinople in 381 and from that time on was driven out of the Byzantine orthodoxy. New heresies diverged from the accepted dogmas as to the nature of Christ in two opposite directions. The orthodox view was, then and now, that there are *two natures* in Christ (human and divine) but *one person*. The followers of the Syrian priest, Nestorios (V-1), claimed that there are in Christ *two natures* and *two persons*. Eutychēs, archimandrite of a monastery near Constantinople, fought the Nestorians so hard that he fell into the opposite error. He created the heresy named after him—Eutychianism—and later Monophysitism. Eutychēs claimed that the divine and the human are so blended in the person of Christ as to constitute but one nature; Christ is *of* two natures but *in* one nature. The Monophysites declared more bluntly that there is in Christ but *one nature* and *one person*.

These Christological differences went very close to rending apart the seamless coat of Christ. The various kinds of Christians hated one another more than they hated the infidels. The Nestorian heresy was condemned by the third Council, in Ephesos, 431; the fourth Council, in Chalcedon, 451, anathematized the Eutychians as well as the Nestorians.

Condemnations and curses were rapidly enforced by ecclesiastical and lay officials, and the final result was that many good men were either killed or banished. We may assume that men who prefer to abandon their homes and business and suffer all the rigors of poverty and exile rather than recant or dissemble their religious thoughts—that such men must be exceptionally brave and good. The empire impoverished itself to the profit of foreign countries. The Arians had been driven westward; the Monophysites swarmed out into Syria and into Egypt; the Nestorians emigrated eastward, and the school of Edessa was their main center until it was closed by the emperor Zēnōn the Isaurian in 489. This caused a further dispersion of them; the Nestorian seat was in Seleuceia-Ctēsiphōn in 498, in Baghdād in 762. They swarmed all over Asia as far as the Pacific Ocean.

There was a medical school in Edessa, and the Nestorians found themselves there in a scientific community. They translated many Greek books of philosophy and science into Syriac and these Syrian books were later translated into Arabic. The "scientific road" from Alexandria to Baghdād passed through Edessa.[40] Thus would be completed in the fulness of time a remarkable cycle. Greek science was born in Asia Minor, then flourished in Greece proper, chiefly in Athens, then in Alexandria, and back to Asia, Pergamon, Constantinople, Edessa, Baghdād.

The move from Athens to Alexandria was due to political causes, that from Egypt and Greece to Asia very largely to religious ones. Every persecution is a centrifugal force. The "good Christians" drove the Arians, Nestorians, Eutychians

---

[40] It may be that when the school of Edessa (modern Urfa) was closed in 489 some of the Nestorians took refuge at Jundīshāpūr in Khūzistān, where a medical school was functioning; some of the pagans may have resorted to the same place, which became a center of dispersion of Greek culture in the Near East (*Intro. 1*, 435). Jundīshāpūr is at a considerable distance east of Baghdād, however.

further and further away and thus helped to diffuse Greek science in the Asiatic world.

We have dealt so long with Christian sects that the reader might forget the existence of pagans. There were still pagans, especially among the least educated and the best educated people. There were undoubtedly pagans (*pagani,* "rustics" in the isolated places, and on the other hand, the "intellectuals," the outstanding philosophers, were reluctant to accept Christianity and reject Hellenism. This was especially true of those who were privileged to teach in the Academy of Athens, which became, as it were, a center of resistance to the new religion. Therefore, Justinian closed it in 529.

This is a fateful date, which I consider to be the best symbol of the end of an age. The same year witnessed the foundation of Monte Cassino by St. Benedict (VI-1). Seven teachers of the Academy escaped to the court of the king of Persia, Chosroës, and remained there a few years until a treaty of peace enabled them to return.

As to the empire itself, a part of its strength and of its virtue was drained away by each persecution; some of the best men were driven into exile some of the worst rose to the surface.

The final transition from paganism to Christianity was difficult enough. It implied conflict of loyalties, the destruction of vested interests and the precarious establishment of new ones. Moreover, the process was reversed during Julian's reign. The situation was enormously aggravated, however, by profound discords within the new Christian world. The Arians went up and down, the Nestorians and the Monophysites were relentlessly persecuted. By the beginning of the Sixth Century the Byzantine empire was weakened in many ways, chiefly because it had lost the good will of its own subjects. The persecution of heterodoxies had been continued too long, too many good people had been driven into sulkiness and resentment or even into exile. Refugees carried Greek science to the East and helped to prepare intellectual weapons outside the Christian world, weapons which would soon be used against it.

The Byzantine empire had finally become orthodox in fact as well as in name, but it was totering; its material improverishment was great, the spiritual one extreme. The time would soon be ripe for Arabic conquests and no dike would be strong enough to resist the Islamic flood.

Modern science is the continuation and fructification of Greek science and would not exist without it. Our lectures suggest another conclusion, however, which is more timely today than it ever was.

Intolerance and persecution are self-defeating. The hunger for knowledge and the search for truth can never be eradicated; the best that persecution can do is to drive out non-conformists. In the end this will be a loss not for humanity but for their own country. The refugees carry wisdom and knowledge from one place to another and mankind goes on.

Greek scholars were driven out of the Greek world and helped to develop Arabic science. Later the Arabic writing was translated into Latin, into Hebrew, and into our own vernaculars. The treasure of Greek science, most of it at least, came to us through that immense detour. We should be grateful not only to the inventors, but also to all the men thanks to those courage and obstinacy the ancient treasure finally reached us and helped to make us what we are.